Attention Deficit Disorder

David Sosin, M.D. & Myra Sosin

Teacher Created Materials, Inc.

Cover Design by Darlene Spivak

Made in U.S.A.

ISBN 1-55734-883-9

Order Number TCM 883

Table of Contents

Introduction

As a married couple who are a doctor and a teacher as well as parents of our own Attention Deficit Disorder child, we have a unique perspective to contribute to the study of ADD. Because we live with ADD on a daily basis, we know just how real it is. Daily, we deal with its frustrations and triumphs.

Once one is sensitized to and educated about the realities of ADD, one cannot help but notice it in the classroom. In a classroom of thirty students, two or three are very likely to have ADD. Many of these have never been diagnosed or treated. The teacher has a special opportunity to recognize and help these children. It is tragic to hear of children, year after year, described as inattentive, class clowns, bored, or "bright but lazy" and to see diagnoses of ADD missed, even though the symptoms should be known and recognized by every trained teacher.

We hope that this book will be helpful to the teacher. First, we describe what the teacher is likely to encounter when he or she has an ADD child in the classroom. Then, we offer specific strategies that the teacher can utilize in making this child more successful in school and in life. The list of classroom modifications can be used as a centerpiece of a teacher/parent/counselor/administrator conference to make an individual plan for each ADD student in order to enhance the child's possibilities for success.

What Is ADD?

Typical ADD Children

Do you know someone who is bright and creative but tends to be messy, scattered, and disorganized? Check the following list of traits:

- ◆ is easily distracted
- ◆ forgets often
- ◆ loses things
- ◆ seems to be always on the go
- ◆ procrastinates
- ◆ is messy
- ◆ has trouble staying on task
- ◆ has many unfinished projects
- ◆ dislikes paperwork
- ◆ has problems remaining seated
- ◆ has trouble concentrating through lectures or meetings

Do you know someone who is bright and creative but tends to be messy, scattered, and disorganized?

How many of these traits describe a person you know? On the other hand, this person can be innovative and artistic. He or she is an original thinker. The person is intuitive, sincere, and empathic—someone you can talk to. This person usually is direct and to the point (although sometimes a bit blunt—in fact, even tactless).

As a student, he might be like little Albert, who has failed math, seems bored by school, and cannot get along with the other children because he always insists on doing his own thing. He is socially awkward and "different." When the others go out to play, he would rather stay in and play his violin. He does so poorly at his school work that his parents and teachers worry that he might be intellectually impaired.

ADD is an inherited neurobiological disorder which becomes evident in early childhood and usually continues throughout a person's life.

Young Ben is impulsive, disorganized, and argumentative. You never know what he is going to get into next. He has a million ideas and imaginative projects. Ben is the kind of person who might go out and fly a metallic kite in a thunderstorm!

As you probably have guessed by now, the parents and teachers of Albert Einstein and Benjamin Franklin did not have too much to worry about, but as youngsters, these boys were quite trying to the adults around them. Of course, not all students will grow up to be Einstein or Franklin. But many students with their kind of potential exist in our classrooms. Often, like Einstein and Franklin, they seem to march to different drummers. And often, like Einstein and Franklin, these students have Attention Deficit Disorder.

Defining ADD

ADD is an inherited neurobiological disorder which becomes evident in early childhood and usually continues throughout a person's life. Although ADD may manifest itself in many different ways from one individual to the next, the central theme is a difficulty in sustaining focus and concentration.

The Brain as Director

An analogy may help to clarify how the ADD brain functions. Imagine the brain as a television director monitoring the control panel as many cameras are sending back pictures of a complex event, such as a football game or a political convention. In just seconds, the director must decide which of the incoming barrage of images to send out to the audience. As each camera switches its focus, the director is the center of a blur of activity, constantly vigilant, focusing and refocusing, selecting images for the audience. At the same time, the director is directing the camera operators to focus on potentially interesting images, scanning for the best and most telling selections for the audience. Many images seem compelling; however, the director's job is to select, making the story not only exciting but also organized and cohesive for the audience.

But what if all of the images are equally compelling? What if the director just cannot select one over the other? Obviously, he becomes more and more frustrated and ineffective. The director cannot do the job, which is to make decisions and choices while being bombarded with multiple inputs.

The director's dilemma is a good analogy to explain what the ADD youngster goes through in trying to stay focused on what is important in everyday activities. The good director is capable of sticking to the central theme at a given moment. The ADDer does not have a competent director on board to throw the switches. In a classroom, for instance, the teacher's lecture, the bird singing outside the window, the posters on the wall, the two kids talking nearby, the noise in the hall, the clock on the wall, the hunger pangs signaling that lunch time is near, the memory of this morning's argument at home, and next Saturday's planned trip to the circus are all competing for attention in the ADD student's brain. All of these inputs are equally compelling. Like the unskilled director, the ADDer cannot select which input is the most important and becomes confused and frustrated by these choices.

There is no doubt in the scientific community that ADD is real.

ADD Is Real

There is no doubt in the scientific community that ADD is real. It is not a "yuppie disease," an excuse, or a cop-out for an undisciplined child. ADD has been documented by years of observation and, more recently, by modern brain imaging technology. Legally, a student with ADD is covered by both US Public Law 94-1942 (Part B of the Individuals with Disabilities Education Act) and Section 504 of the Federal Rehabilitation Act of 1973. Under these laws, schools are legally required to make accommodations for this student (Fowler, 1992).

ADD and Intelligence

Most ADDers do not have problems of intelligence. The majority of ADD students are of at least average intelligence, and many are well above average. Nor is ADD a result of "brain damage," as in a malformation or obvious injury. The human brain, however, is highly complex, and we do not fully understand all of its subtle physiological and chemical actions. According to Dr. Larry B. Silver (1992), most ADDers have average or above average intelligence but still have academic difficulties because of the way their brains or nervous systems function (p. 10).

3

Is ADD on the Increase?

ADD is not a new phenomenon, although it is receiving increased publicity. ADD has always been with us but has not always been recognized. These children used to be called "hyperactive" because many of them were noticeably unable to stay still, especially in classrooms. However, in 1972 educational psychologist Virginia Douglas correctly realized that the most important feature of this phenomenon was distractibility, resulting in a difficulty in sustaining attention. So the new name, Attention Deficit Disorder, was born. This insight accounts for a seeming "explosion" of ADD cases in today's classrooms.

We now know that not all people with ADD are hyperactive. Those with hyperactivity are characterized as having ADHD. Increased physical activity is only one of a complex of symptoms that characterize ADD or ADHD. Today, professionals have identified the following as the core traits of ADD:

> ADD is not a new phenomenon, although it is receiving increased publicity.

- ◆ impulsivity
- ◆ distractibility
- ◆ overactivity

Each of these traits will be discussed at length in later chapters.

ADD Myths and Realities

The mistaken belief that increased activity is the major component of ADD might be the source of one of the more popular myths about this condition, which is that only boys have it. Whether by biology or social conditioning, boys have been diagnosed as being hyperactive at about six to ten times the rate for girls. The boy to girl ratio, however, probably is much closer to 50–50. Society expects that "boys will be boys" and bounce off walls, while conditioning little girls to act like "ladies," which means that they should be quiet, patient, and less physical in their activities. Now that we are becoming more aware of ADD in girls, we may notice more subtle expressions of hyperactivity. A girl bouncing her foot, tapping her pencil, playing with her buttons or bows, or twirling a strand of hair as she stares out the window might escape attention, while the little boy's more rambunctious actions gain notice. The little girl is equally "tuned out," but the little boy, the "squeaky wheel," gets the attention.

The most popular myth about ADD is that it disappears when childhood ends. Somewhere along the line, some prominent professionals in the field incorrectly concluded that ADD usually burns itself out by the late teens. This notion persists today among many educators, psychologists, physicians, and other professionals. Experts now believe that in a large proportion of ADDers, the condition lasts a lifetime. How, then, does one account for the mistaken notion that ADD disappears by adolescence? One answer might be that the symptoms do not disappear—the kids do! ADD students experience incredible difficulties in school. For this reason, a disproportionate number of these students, although they may be highly intelligent, drop out of school. The phenomenon of the bright and charming young person who is working at flipping hamburgers, boxing groceries, or pumping gas, even though this person seems to have so much "potential," leads one to wonder how many of these dropouts have undiagnosed ADD or some other learning disability.

Another reason that we may not notice ADD so much as children go into adolescence is that many of these children have developed coping skills as they mature. They are much less likely to act out in childish ways, and the manifestations of ADD might be much more subtle. Recent conservative estimates suggest that up to five percent of the total population of the United States has ADD. These statistics do not cover just children. Some published estimates of ADD in the general population go as high as fifteen percent. In an average classroom population of thirty children, the teacher can expect one or two of these children to have ADD (Fowler, 1992). The middle or high school teacher whose classes change every hour can expect to see several ADDers in a day.

ADD and Teachers

There still is a major lack of awareness in the teaching profession about the realities of Attention Deficit Disorder. Although teacher education is making strides in disseminating information, there still is a vast under-recognition of ADD in the classroom. Teachers and counselors frequently tell parents that their child daydreams, is inattentive and fidgety, and does not do homework but that the child is really smart and could do the work if he or she tried harder. Sadly, teachers are giving a description of a youngster with Attention Deficit Disorder, often without recognizing that they are doing so.

If a youngster is not working up to potential, one of the first things that should pop into a teacher's mind is, "Could this child have Attention Deficit Disorder?" The important reason for this question is that ADD is a condition that can be rapidly and successfully treated, allowing the youngster to focus, concentrate on school work, and start achieving success. If the teacher's and counselor's recommendations lead to professional diagnosis which finds that the condition is not ADD, then no harm is done. However, if this diagnosis is

There still is a major lack of awareness in the teaching profession about the realities of Attention Deficit Disorder.

5

missed, the potential for harm to the child's academic potential, social and family relationships, and self-esteem is great.

Discovering My Own ADD

For as long as I can remember, including years in medical school and psychiatric training in New York City, I had been deeply aware that some youngsters suffered from hyperactivity which was very responsive to stimulant medication. Although no one quite understood how, clearly these youngsters had significant therapeutic effects from being placed on stimulants, which calmed them down and gave parents and teachers a much easier time in handling them. The youngsters themselves always reported feeling better. As my years as a psychiatrist passed, I medicated many children for their hyperactivity. I liked seeing these youngsters because I felt I could do something meaningful for them. It all seemed so simple and natural.

> As I looked at my son, I realized that if he has ADD, so do I.

What was not so simple was coming to grips with my growing realization that my own son, who was about ten at the time, was blossoming into a full-fledged ADDer. Now, my passionate interest in this disorder began to make sense to me. I already had begun to realize that ADD never truly goes away. As I looked at my son, I realized that if he has ADD, so do I. I wondered if during all those years that I had found this subject fascinating I had been trying to figure out myself, as well as my patients.

Tracing the Roots in Childhood

The more I studied the subject, the more I realized that so many of my personality traits were not unique to me. I had always felt different. When other kids were interested in fitting in and conforming, I went the other way. Looking back at my own father and his constant motion, it is clear that he had ADD. He had a restlessness about him which he discharged by physical activity. Before becoming an avid fisherman, he was a tennis player and bicycle racer. From the time I was four, my dad used to take my brother and me fishing with him. Soon, I would grow restless, tire of holding a pole, and would wander off, observing nature and developing a passion for animals and plants. I was on the move, like the young hunter, constantly looking for new stimuli.

On the other hand, I assumed that my deep sense of fair play and justice was influenced by my mother, an attorney, who often explained the law, justice, and fairness to me. I now know that this sense of fair play also is a strong ADD trait. Unlike many ADDers, I did well in school. Even math was not especially difficult. Luckily, I grew up when the work ethic was still in place and electronic diversions few. I had many hobbies by the time my family got its first television, a monstrous box with a twelve-inch screen. My creative side enjoyed art and drawing, and my insatiable curiosity drove me to take things apart and search through drawers and attics for hidden treasures.

My Own ADD Traits

Although I was a good student, my ADD did manifest itself. I used to get into trouble with my mouth (and still do!). I constantly was cited for talking in class, and I tangled with a number of teachers, usually the rigid and dogmatic ones. I was not very diplomatic. When I knew that a teacher was wrong, I would let her know it, frequently in the presence of others (mistake!). I remember a number of teachers who aroused so much resentment that I had to force myself to learn from them, telling myself that they did not personally own the subject and that my feelings should not stand in the way of learning. Looking back, the teachers I really liked were kind, fair, consistent, and had basic human decency. These positive attributes in teachers facilitate learning for all students. I now know that students' emotional responses to teachers constitute the affective component of learning, where positive feelings toward the teacher make learning easier and more enjoyable for all students, not just ADDers. I did have a few close friends who shared my interests, but I tended to be a loner. Nature was my passion. I also related well to adult mentors, such as a kindly physician friend who gave me my first microscope.

> Although I was a good student, my ADD did manifest itself.

Using My Own ADD to Help Others

Looking back on my own childhood has helped me to better understand my patients. As I got more deeply involved in helping with their problems, I realized that I, too, still had similar problems which affected my family and me. Knowing that many of these traits derive from ADD helps me to deal with them more effectively. My style of divergent thinking is echoed in most of my patients. As an adult, I still struggle with my tendencies to be messy, disorganized, distractible, and a big procrastinator (just ask my wife about writing this book together!).

About five years ago, I made a decision to formally specialize in the treatment of ADD, since I had been doing it informally for 35 years. My plan was to start a journey of discovery which would help my son, myself, and my patients. On this journey, I would ask patients about certain behavior traits or styles, sometimes ones that I had observed in my son or me. When I see youngsters struggling with school and learning, my heart goes out to them. I can perceive the dilemmas of the ADDer from the earliest years into adulthood and have constant ongoing feedback about crucial issues from my patients, some of whom are quoted (under pseudonyms) in this book.

Concluding Remarks

The classroom teacher has a great role to play in the recognition and treatment of the youngster who has ADD. School is a particularly difficult and stressful situation for most ADD youngsters, so the teacher may have a chance to observe behaviors which might not be evident in other situations. The teacher has the most opportunity to modify the school situation so that the youngster can be successful. Going the extra mile for the ADD student may yield wonderful results. These students may be some of the most creative and intelligent people on the planet. They may be gifted with the ability to come up with new ideas and inventions which contribute to the betterment of humanity. The majority of people with Attention Deficit Disorder are capable of completing higher levels of education and becoming successful in a wide range of careers. However, they all recognize that their accomplishments usually come through perseverance and very hard work. The intervention of a wise and compassionate teacher can enable such a student to use his or her intellect to the fullest. Such a teacher can change a student's life.

Anything I can do to help people to understand ADD makes me know that I have done something important. When I give talks to schools, doctors, and professional groups, I know that I make a difference. Most gratifying of all is taking a human being who is in a state of despair and showing this person that he or she is bright, has much to offer the world, and that embarking on a journey of self-discovery about his or her ADD can lead to an exciting and fulfilling future. My goal is to help educate professionals and the public at large about ADD so that early recognition and treatment of this problem becomes routine.

> The classroom teacher has a great role to play in the recognition and treatment of the youngster who has ADD.

Famous ADDers

Famous People with ADD

Attention Deficit Disorder has its plus side, although the world of school is not always the place where this side shines. The ADDer is different, whereas school pushes conformity. Unfortunately, many ADDers discover their true talents and blossom only upon leaving school. Hallowell and Ratey (1994b) state in *Driven to Distraction*:

> *Throughout history there have been many great men and women who have had learning disabilities that they managed to overcome. Although it cannot be proved he had it, Mozart would be a good example of a person with ADD: impatient, impulsive, distractible, energetic, emotionally needy, creative, innovative, irreverent, and a maverick....Albert Einstein, Edgar Allan Poe, George Bernard Shaw, and Salvador Dali were all expelled from school, and Thomas Edison was at the bottom of his class. Abraham Lincoln and Henry Ford were pronounced by their teachers to show no promise...There is a long, long list of people who achieved greatness in adult life after performing abysmally in school due to undiagnosed learning disabilities. Unfortunately, there is a longer list of those people whose spirits were broken in school* (pp. 43–44).

Attention Deficit Disorder has its plus side, although the world of school is not always the place where this side shines.

9

Edison Fits the ADD Profile

Thomas Alva Edison is a case in point. His extraordinary creative imagination revolutionized the world. He invented the high-speed telegraph, electrified railroad, phonograph, talking motion picture, and, most famous of all, the incandescent lamp. By the time of his death at age 84, he held more than 1,000 patents on his inventions and was a multimillionaire. Yet, his boyhood was difficult, his brushes with school disastrous, and his relationships, particularly with his father, trying. Biographer Margaret Cousins (1965) describes an incident in which young Edison's father whipped him in the public square for burning his father's barn to the ground. Alva had set a little fire inside the barn just to see what it would do. Edison said that his father thought he was stupid. His father often said that he could not understand his son and that Edison lacked common sense. He was trying, he was vexing, he was forever curious and forever asking questions which most adults considered foolish. Punishment seemed unsuccessful in changing Edison.

> The role of a supportive teacher (in this case, also a supportive parent) cannot be overemphasized in turning what could be failure into success.

Due to illness and family moves, young Edison did not enter formal schooling until the age of eight. His harsh teacher soon resorted to the use of a leather strap to control him. Edison's schoolmaster said he was addled and considered him backward, but the youngster's mother, a former teacher, decided to school him at home and managed to get him excited about learning. The results of this excitement about learning revolutionized the world. The role of a supportive teacher (in this case, also a supportive parent) cannot be overemphasized in turning what could be failure into success.

A Profile of Albert Einstein

Albert Einstein was such a mentor to young people. The young Einstein is well known to have been the student whose grades were among the lowest in his rigid German school, which he hated passionately. Like most children with ADD, he was an insatiable questioner who often drove teachers to distraction by asking questions they could not answer. How fascinating to see the roots of his later work in some of the questions he asked, such as, "What is light made of?" It is perhaps comforting to remember that Einstein, a lifelong musician, rebelled at practicing the violin, especially playing repetitious and boring scales. He could not sustain more than a few minutes of practice without becoming distracted and having his attention wander to something else.

Young Albert had a reputation for being stubborn, but he knew, even as a youth, what he did and did not like and want to learn. As a child, he refused to participate in the militaristic games and exercises that were played by his schoolmates. Of course, years later he gained an international reputation as a pacifist. His parents worried about his shyness. Often, during group activities, he seemed to be else-where—and he was! He told his parents he was "just thinking." Fortunately, although relationships with other children, teachers, and his father often were difficult, Albert's mother believed in his abilities, and a young physician cousin acted as a mentor, nurturing and supporting his curiosities.

Many years later, by this time world famous, Einstein himself was a beloved mentor. He would tutor neighborhood children in Princeton, New Jersey, in arithmetic, telling them to stop by any time they had problems with math—he said he remembered what it was like to have difficulties with arithmetic!

ADD and Creativity

Almost all experts agree that extraordinary creativity can be a hall-mark of ADD. Nobody is sure just why this is true, although there are some tantalizing theories. Hallowell and Ratey (1994) may have an answer as to why this creativity is so closely related to ADD. They see creativity as a more positive manifestation of ADD impulsivity.

Howard Gardner (Gardner, 1983) has done groundbreaking work with his theories of multiple intelligences. According to Gardner, creativity is one of many different kinds of intelligence that a person might display. Unfortunately, schools and society in general reward some types of intelligence (mathematical, for example) more than others (such as interpersonal intelligence).

Another tantalizing theory about what makes the creative ADDer tick comes from Thomas Hartmann (1993), who has come up with the "hunter/farmer" personality distinction. He theorizes that in primitive times, society was divided into the hunters, restless types whose survival depended on constantly scanning for tiny details, being hypersensitive, and taking in every stimulus. Their farmer contemporaries were content to stay in one place, planting and patiently waiting to reap their harvests. It would have been difficult for a hunter to be a farmer or vice versa. Each had his place in the social structure. Unfortunately, says Hartmann, today's society is not set up for the hunter. Sitting in one's chair in school for six hours and being silent for most of this time is not what the little hunter's genes predispose him to do. Little farmers, on the other hand, will do fine.

Almost all experts agree that extraordinary creativity can be a hallmark of ADD.

11

Concluding Remarks

The teacher who welcomes individuality and creativity, even if the student deviates from the norm, and finds ways to incorporate this creativity into the classroom and into assignments, is very likely to have success with ADD students. The teacher who expects all students to be and act one way and to conform to all of the same demands and expectations is very likely to break their spirits and teach them nothing but to hate school.

Distractibility

What Is Distractibility?

Of the three core traits seen in ADD (distractibility, impulsivity, and overactivity), the one that causes the most problems for the student and teacher is distractibility. In fact, distractibility is the most pervasive of the traits seen in all ADDers. Distractibility means difficulty in remaining focused on any one thing for very long. Even though the student is physically present in class, one could describe him as not really being there because his mind is far away.

In fact, distractibility is the most pervasive of the traits seen in all ADDers.

The tendency to become easily distracted plagues ADDers for all of their lives. One of the most dramatic and graphic descriptions of this problem came from an ADD adult when he experienced the benefits of stimulant medication for the first time. He stated with great emotion and satisfaction that, "I feel as though a cloud or fog has lifted between me and the rest of the world. For the first time in my life I feel that I'm really here."

In the classroom, distractibility is an automatic response to boredom. The more interesting, dynamic, and involved the teacher is with the subject matter, the less likely any student, not just an ADDer, is to drift off into his own world. Another problem arises when the

13

teacher is not being very clear. The ADD youngster is lost and cannot seem to catch up. The student's mind drifts to another place in order to avoid the confusion and frustration of not understanding.

Difficulties with Auditory Processing

Distractibility is worsened by another problem that most ADDers have with auditory processing, the term for how the brain sorts out incoming auditory information. ADD individuals typically have acute hearing. But problems arise because the person's attention gets diverted automatically to the loudest ambient sound. A common example of such a situation occurs when trying to have a conversation in a crowded, noisy restaurant. A generalized din, punctuated by noises and bits of conversation, provides a steady stream of distractions, making it difficult to follow what someone sitting across from you is saying. ADDers have the worst time in such situations. Many ADD children have had their hearing checked, only to find that it is perfectly intact but that they are easily distracted by auditory processing problems. Thus, competing louder sounds, such as outside noise or chattering neighbors, make perceiving what the teacher is saying difficult for the youngster, especially if the student is seated far from the teacher. Teachers must recognize that all of these problems happen automatically to ADD youngsters. Despite the youngster's best efforts to stay consciously tuned in, distractibility is not under conscious control.

> Despite the youngster's best efforts to stay consciously tuned in, distractibility is not under conscious control.

The Torture of Nonparticipatory Classrooms

Most adults with ADD dislike attending meetings because they get bored easily and drift off. However, if they are running the meetings themselves, they are automatically involved and tuned in. The same principle applies to the classroom. Modern strategies emphasize cooperative learning and interactive teaching with a good deal of participation by the student (Grisham & Molinelli, 1995). Such techniques help all youngsters to stay tuned in and are especially valuable for ADDers.

The Affective Component of Learning

Another problem that affects all students, but especially those with ADD, has to do with the affective component of learning, which refers to the feelings a particular teacher elicits in his or her students. In simple terms, if the student likes and respects the teacher, it is much easier for that youngster to stay tuned in and to put forth maximum effort to learn. On the other hand, if the youngster feels that the teacher is mean, lacking in understanding and compassion, or rushes ahead too fast, then that youngster will have a great deal of difficulty learning. The best teachers for ADD students are dynamic and exciting, offering a variety of classroom activities to combat the student's natural tendency to drift off. They also understand the student's problems and can cue the student to stay on task.

Distractibility Outside the Classroom

Distractibility exacts a severe toll outside the classroom when the student tries to complete reading assignments and other homework. Many ADDers report problems with reading, and some have been called dyslexic. Exactly what is going on in an individual who has been labeled dyslexic is not that easy to discern. Treatment strategies to improve the situation are complicated and require a good deal of time. Since dyslexia and ADD overlap each other so frequently, it is vitally important to tease out the presence of ADD in anyone who is considered to have dyslexia. For detailed information on dyslexia, see *Understanding Dyslexia* by Kathleen Hennigh (1995).

If ADD is present, stimulant medication usually improves concentration, speed, and retention in reading. Since so much of one's career as a student depends on having good reading skills, this problem should never be overlooked. The more tedious, boring, or difficult the material, the more natural it is for ADDers and other students to drift off the subject matter out of boredom or frustration. Even though the student knows how important it is to stick to the topic and keep reading, he will frequently have no recollection about anything he has just read. Furthermore, he quickly grows restless and cannot sustain his reading efforts for more than a few minutes.

Many ADDers report problems with reading, and some have been called dyslexic.

Classroom Strategies

Cooperative learning and other interactive techniques tend to keep the distractible students on their toes. Close monitoring and private signals may help the teacher pull the student back if his attention begins to drift. Building small breaks for physical movement into a lesson can be helpful, as can varying activities during a single class period. Arranging the classroom and the particular child's seating in a manner where he is least likely to be disturbed by outside noise, views, or other students can help the distractible child and so can an administrative decision to keep classroom interruptions and changes in schedule to an absolute minimum. Setting up the classroom into learning areas or stations, including some which offer privacy, can help some children to focus. Some experts say, however, that tables of four or five children, which are quite a typical configuration in modern classrooms, may prove distracting for the ADD child, who might be better off at his own desk. The introductory cooperative learning information and exercises on pages 16 through 21 may help you in your classroom.

Whole-Classroom Readiness and Activities

Easing into Cooperative Learning

Prepare your students for cooperative learning by conducting whole-class cooperative activities. Whole-class activities are especially conducive to creating a comfortable, safe environment in which students have some knowledge and understanding of one another. It is helpful to ease into the cooperative experience since many students may never have had the experience of cooperative interaction.

Parallel Players and Pre-Cooperative Learners

The students in your classroom probably have some experience in cooperative learning. However, children at any skill level or age who have not been exposed to cooperative learning often make a slow transition. Early childhood education experts tell us that the younger the children in a group are, the less comfortable they will feel with group participation. Most toddlers and preschool age children parallel play. This means that they play near each other at separate tasks. It is important to note that children learn to play together. It is not their initial instinct.

Becoming a cooperative learner is a process. Many adults have yet to master the concept in their work situations. Cooperation in a group is a difficult skill, and only years of practice can ensure a student's mastery.

To ease into cooperative learning, focus on pre-cooperative learning skills. Teachers can focus on the idea of children learning how to get along within the classroom setting. Concepts such as sharing and taking turns are understood by pre-cooperative learners, and while a pre-cooperative learner may not always feel comfortable sharing or taking turns, these ideas are ones they will certainly recognize.

Finally, be aware of your students. When they have had enough of a cooperative activity, turn to a less stressful and more autonomous one.

Partner Activities

Cooperation is an important component in any classroom. When children cooperate, they have the opportunity to think about and assimilate new ideas.

Use the whole-class activities on page 18 to nurture the cooperative atmosphere within your classroom. To help ease your students into the concept of cooperative learning, allow them this time to work with one partner only.

It is important that the transition into cooperative learning be a comfortable one for your children. You may wish to have your students become very secure with partner activities before beginning other cooperative activities, or you may find it beneficial to use both group and partner activities, depending on your student's learning needs.

Reprinted from TCM 654 Cooperative Learning Activities for Social Studies, *Teacher Created Materials, 1995*

Whole-Classroom Readiness and Activities

1. **Personal Journal**

   This activity can be used for individual and partner interaction. Have each child start a journal. When any classroom activity ends, have the children draw and write about the activity. Each journal entry can be dated with a notation about the activity to which it refers.

   Let the students know that this journal is for them. There is no one right way to do it. It is just for fun. They can look back on it and remember what they did in class and how they felt about it.

   Partners: Assign a partner to each child. Partners will discuss their journal entries. This activity will not only help children relax in a cooperative learning environment, but it will also build cooperative and communicative skills in a nonthreatening way.

2. **Rest and Remember**

   This activity will help children prepare for—or unwind after—a classroom activity or special event. Have the children go to their seats or rest their heads on their desks. You may wish to dim the classroom lights or play soft music. While the students are resting, ask them to think about the activity they just completed. Ask them to picture the activity, see it as a mental movie, and decide what they liked and did not like about it. Ask them how they felt—happy, sad, angry, excited, etc. Ask them what they would like to do differently next time they work in their groups. You may then wish to follow up by reading the students a short, happy poem or story.

   Partners: Have students talk with a partner immediately following the "Rest and Remember" exercise, discussing what they liked about the activity they have just completed. This can also be another opportunity to use their journals.

3. **Letter Home**

   This activity is helpful in encouraging language and memory skills. It also engenders parental and parent/child participation in your program.

   Have students write letters and illustrate what they did in their cooperative learning activity.

   Have the students return the letters and share what their parents thought about the activity and their participation. This activity will also help you to stay in contact with parents consistently, rather than just when there is a problem.

   Partners: Have partners view each other's letter home and make one positive comment or compliment. This activity encourages students to support each other, and it promotes self-esteem.

Reprinted from TCM 651 Cooperative Learning Activities for Language Arts, *Teacher Created Materials, 1995*

Whole-Classroom Readiness and Activities

1. **Shoe Hunt/Partner Hunt:** Students can use the pattern on page 19 to color two matching shoes. They will write their names on the provided lines. Half the students can then put one "shoe" into a box, bowl, or other container and leave the second shoe on their desks. The other half will take turns picking a shoe and matching it to the one on the owner's desk. The student whose shoe was picked will then become that student's partner. Each set of partners will walk together to find out three things about one another. They can write what they have learned on the shoes. Use the completed shoes for a bulletin board display.

   This activity is a good icebreaker for shy children or those who do not know each other. Used at the beginning of the school year, it will set the stage for building cooperative teams based on friendly interaction.

2. **Secret Secret:** Choose a leader to begin. Have students stand in a circle. The first person tells the second person a secret. It is then repeated until it reaches the end of the circle and is said aloud. Have the person who began the secret and the person who heard it last compare the differences in the secret. This activity will help students to understand the importance of listening carefully in their cooperative groups.

3. **Walking Through the Neighborhood, I Saw a...:** This is a whole-class participation alphabet game. Students stand or sit in a circle. Choose someone to lead with the sentence starter, "I was walking through the neighborhood, and I saw a..." He or she fills in the blank with something that starts with the letter "A." The next person in the group must think of something that begins with the letter "B," and so on with the rest of the alphabet. (If there are more students after "Z," return to the beginning of the alphabet.)

   You may wish to begin the activity by holding a whole-class discussion about the possible things that a child might see during a walk through the neighborhood. You may also alter the first sentence as desired. For example, you may begin, "In my house I saw a...," or "I went to the city and saw a...."

4. **Alphabet Name Game:** Give each student a soup bowl with alphabet macaroni or paper letters. Write a word on the board. The first students to spell the word with his/her alphabet letters is the winner of the round. Next, have students work in pairs to spell as many words as they can with their letters, making a written list of the words they spell. Beginning readers can spell their names by locating the appropriate alphabet letters. This activity increases letter recognition and spelling skills while at the same time introducing friendly competition. (You may also play noncompetitively.)

5. **Learn to Take Turns:** Explore the many ways of taking turns. For example, vote, flip coins, let a neutral party decide, draw straws, draw names, guess a number or letter, or simply take turns being a leader.

Reprinted from TCM 656 Cooperative Learning Activities for Math, *Teacher Created Materials, 1995*

Whole-Classroom Readiness and Activities

Shoe Pattern

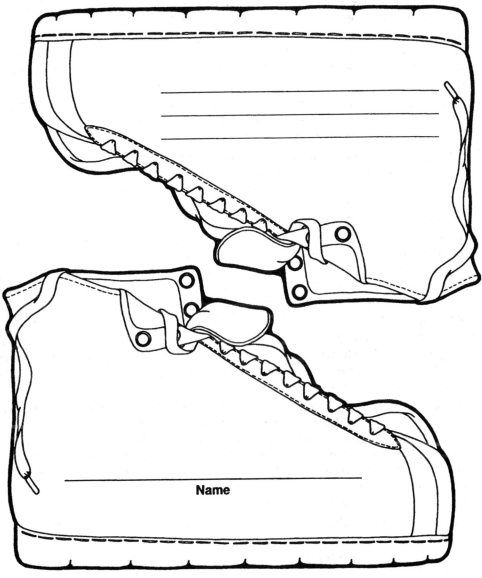

Name

Reprinted from TCM 656 Cooperative Learning Activities for Math, *Teacher Created Materials,* 1995

Whole-Classroom Readiness and Activities

Dear _____,

Here is a picture of what my cooperative learning group did today.

I helped my group by...

_____

_____

My favorite part was...

_____

_____

Love,

_____

- -

Parent Comments:

_____

_____

Note from the teacher: Thank you for supporting your child in his/her cooperative learning experience. I welcome all parent volunteers. Please write your number here if you would like a phone call.

Thank you,

_____

Name: _____

Name of Child: _____

Phone: _____

Reprinted from TCM 656 Cooperative Learning Activities for Math, *Teacher Created Materials,* 1995

How We Work Together

1. When we work in groups, we always take turns.

2. We listen when other people talk.

3. Everyone in the group gets to have a turn.

4. If we cannot agree on something, we vote.

5. If we have a problem, we try to work it out. We do not fight.

6. If we do not know what to do or if we have a question, we ask the group first and then the teacher.

Reprinted from TCM 654 Cooperative Learning Activities for Social Studies, *Teacher Created Materials, 1995*

Concluding Remarks

In summary, the best way for a teacher to be effective in handling problems of distractibility is to have a true understanding of what the youngster is going through. When the teacher admonishes Johnny to sit still, look straight ahead, and pay attention, what really is happening is that Johnny is on auto pilot and cannot control his attention just by saying, "O.K., I'll pay attention." Actually, Johnny is doing the best he can under the circumstances. Correctly prescribed medication can make a positive difference in distractibility. Teachers need to communicate with parents if they notice that an ADD child is not sustaining focus. This feedback should reach the medicating physician so that changes can be made to get the youngster back on track.

Impulsivity

What is Impulsivity?

"Look before you leap," we are constantly admonished, often with very good reason. When we leap, we let go—there is no turning back. So, our very survival may depend on controlling our impulses. Impulsive ADDers seem to be unable to "apply the brakes" to thoughts or actions. They simply cannot take the time to contemplate their actions. The following traits characterize impulsivity:

Impulsive ADDers seem to be unable to "apply the brakes" to thoughts or actions.

- ◆ acting before thinking

- ◆ jumping from one activity to another

- ◆ calling or talking out, interrupting conversations

- ◆ having difficulty waiting for a turn or waiting in line

- ◆ blurting out feelings or ideas—may be seen as blunt, tactless, or insensitive

- ◆ making decisions, even major ones, without planning or consideration of consequences

- ◆ acting reckless, fearless, or thrill-seeking—engaging in dangerous behaviors without recognizing need for caution

23

- repeating problem behaviors—not learning from past
- jumping into new experiences without first reading instructions or checking directions

Effects of Impulsivity

Impulsivity can be a real problem for students and their teachers. The impulsive student can disrupt a class by talking out of turn, blurting out comments or answers, clowning or joking at the wrong time, or turning a discussion off track. The child can be annoying to teachers and fellow students by interrupting conversations or pushing and shoving in the lunch line. The child who is thwarted may become angry.

Teachers have described the impulsive child in many ways:

- "She says whatever pops into her head."
- "He rushes headlong into his work, is the first one finished, and does every problem wrong."
- "He does not read or follow instructions."

Teachers wonder—does the child do these things to make them angry? Is this a bad or naughty child? A manipulator? Or is the child just immature?

The Child's Perspective

Actually, these children are not consciously naughty or disobedient. Often, they are shocked to be told that they are doing something wrong. Impulsivity is a part of their very natures. Gary, today a physician, recognizes the effects of impulsivity as he looks back at his early school years and his reputation as a troublemaker:

> "Grades one to three were spent in disarray. In the first grade I received an 'F' in deportment and often cried after school. I had no idea that I was bad. That is my first recollection that I was different, and it was the beginning of a near lifetime of disappointment in myself and deep shame which was reinforced by teachers....On entrance to fourth grade, I was quickly branded as a behavior problem and held the school record for writing 'I will be a good boy' until I felt like a very bad boy indeed. I shake as I remember those years. My classmates' derision marked my soul....I was nearly expelled from eighth grade. One important thing. They were into testing then. I consistently scored at college level in reading and math. Yet, I consistently got D's or F's academically."

> **Impulsivity can be a real problem for students and their teachers.**

Another student, Mark, felt targeted by his classmates and unprotected by the adults at school who saw him as a nuisance. His impulsive inability to think before he acted and his lack of playground survival skills led him to defend himself by using offensive language and inappropriate behaviors. His uninhibited comments about classmates being boring led his fourth grade teachers to label him the class clown. Janet, on the other hand, now grown up, married, and a mother, looks back on her reputation as a malicious person:

"I was accused of mischievousness that I just do not have in my mind or heart. I got accused of a lot of things during those years. I guess my behavior was different from others, that I seemed capable of hurting other people. I was devastated by these accusations and withdrew....97 percent of the time, I did not know what I was doing wrong with people."

Problem Behaviors

Obviously, the lack of ability to perceive social cues from other students and from teachers, and to perceive or control the effect one is having on others can lead the youngster into unsuccessful, frustrating social encounters, disciplinary problems, and lifelong problems with self-esteem. ADDers often leap before they look—literally, as well as figuratively. They log in extraordinary numbers of emergency room visits and might be labeled as "accident prone." Their grades can be affected because they work impulsively on paper. They might not read a question thoroughly, jotting down answers without thinking problems or answers through.

Adolescents court disaster because of impulsive behavior. They may push the limits of speed and their own abilities when they are on the road. They may experiment with alcohol and drugs because these substances look like "fun" or have sex without protection. Delayed gratification seems like a foreign concept to these youngsters.

Intervention Strategies

The teacher may be effective at counseling such young people, guiding them through predicting the consequences of various actions. But peer pressure and the heat of the moment are difficult for youngsters to overcome. Medication can be extremely effective at mitigating impulsivity. Jack says,

"Medication has an organizing factor where it helps me think more clearly. [Without medication] it's like alcohol without being drunk. It's like you have no inhibitions, you loosen up and let it all hang out, which can be good in certain aspects but can be dangerous also."

The teacher may be effective at counseling such young people, guiding them through predicting the consequences of various actions.

25

Randy, 16, says that medication helps him to

> "...grow up. There was a part of me that felt, 'I wish I could be more adult or responsible about things, but I just cannot. It was kind of like it took too much time or it got boring fast.'"

He reports that medication focuses him and helps him to try harder.

The Positive Side of Impulsivity

Like everything else about ADD, impulsivity can have its positive side. Although the word "impulsivity" has negative connotations, more positively connoted words like "spontaneity" or "intuition" or "creativity" may really be the same quality. If one subscribes to the hunter/farmer theory (Hartmann, 1993), one may view the ability to make snap decisions as a survival skill for hunters. Hallowell and Ratey (1994b) write, "What is creativity but impulsivity gone right? One does not plan to have a creative thought. Creative thoughts happen unscheduled. That is to say they are impulsive, the result of an impulse, not a planned course of action....it is out of nowhere, on the wings of impulse, that creativity flies in (p. 177).

Concluding Remarks

The committed teacher's mission is to harness the impulsive/spontaneous/creative energy into productive and positive channels. The impulsive student may be frustrating, but the teacher must remember to preserve the student's dignity. Do not label or name call. Also, do not forget about humor. If you have the chance to respond to ADD impulsivity with anger, discouragement, or humor, choose the latter.

Like everything else about ADD, impulsivity can have its positive side.

Hyperactivity

What Is Hyperactivity?

ADD plus H equals ADHD. The "H" stands for hyperactivity. Before educational psychologist Virginia Douglas (1972) highlighted distractibility and inattention as the essential problems of the condition that we now identify as ADD, most people believed that hyperactivity was the identifying trait (Hallowell and Ratey, 1994b). Teachers were trained to look for restless little boys. The quieter boys and girls who sat in the back of the class, demonstrating all the signs of ADD except the hyperactivity, would go unnoticed. Girls, even very restless ones, would be less noticed because their increased motor activity might take the form of twirling a strand of hair, fidgeting with a pencil, or playing with their nails.

ADHD children typically have difficulty remaining seated and seem to be in constant motion.

What Is ADHD?

ADHD children typically have difficulty remaining seated and seem to be in constant motion. They will twist in their seats, kick their feet, tap their fingers, play with any available objects, and generally give the impression of being driven by motors that cannot be shut off. On the playground, the hyperactive youngster may be harder to distinguish from his peers, but typically he is all over the place and may have a higher instance of accidents.

ADHD children frequently are described as very active and restless from infancy on, getting into everything, breaking toys and destroying household objects. Sometimes parents will report that their ADHD youngster assumed the upright position very early and went from crawling to running seemingly overnight. As these youngsters grow older, they usually are fidgety and have trouble sitting still. Hyperactivity also may take the form of non-stop talking, which some people have characterized as "motor mouth."

On the other hand, these children can appear to be calm and show remarkably long attention spans when they are engrossed in some activity which they enjoy. This absence of constant activity may delude parents and teachers into believing that ADD is not present, even when all of the other symptoms are obvious.

The best strategy to deal with hyperactivity is to help the youngster dissipate excess energy.

Coordination Problems

In addition to hyperactivity, some ADHD children may have coordination problems, which can affect balance, eye-hand coordination, and fine motor performance. Some ADHD children do poorly at sports which require good eye-hand coordination, such as baseball. On the other hand, not all ADHD children are uncoordinated. In fact, some make excellent athletes. The manifestations of hyperactivity are variable from one individual to the next.

Strategies

Teachers and parents need to be aware that hyperactivity is not easily controlled. Asking a child to stop tapping his pencil or to sit still is like asking a bird to stop flying. The best strategy to deal with hyperactivity is to help the youngster dissipate excess energy. However, the child needs to move around through physical activity that is acceptable. In the classroom, assigning ADHD youngsters jobs that keep them moving can be very therapeutic. For example, having Johnny serve as a messenger, attendance monitor, paper passer, or any other job that requires him to move about the classroom or the school can be beneficial. Student monitor passes are included on page 30 for your convenience. Incorporating physical movement into lessons can provide a welcome release for the ADHD youngster. Even getting up to get materials, sharpen a pencil, or put away a book might be enough to release pent up energy. A caring teacher actually can give an ADHD youngster permission in advance to get up and move around in acceptable ways whenever the child finds this necessary. An alert teacher also knows that the hyperactive child's movements (such as playing with a pencil or eraser) may act as a soothing, calming device which actually facilitates attention. If the teacher can do so, he or she should ignore such behaviors unless they are interfering with other students' learning.

Developing prowess in sports can be very positive for ADD youngsters, who frequently report feeling much better after vigorous exercise or games. Encouraging ADD youngsters to get involved in sports is a major part of effective management. If these youngsters do not do well in or like team sports, they especially should be encouraged to take up individual sports, such as swimming, tennis, track, golf, or martial arts, all of which are enjoyed by many ADDers. In addition to discharging energy, sports provide a chance for mastery and social acceptance.

Does Hyperactivity Go Away?

As youngsters move into adolescence, overt hyperactivity frequently diminishes. This decrease in hyperactivity is behind the incorrect assumption (and persistent myth) that hyperactivity syndrome disappears by mid-adolescence. In truth, the "disappearance" of hyperactivity probably is a result of socialization, as well as neurologic maturation. Hyperactive youngsters have learned to dissipate energy through more subtle, less apparent motion. The "hyperactive" child becomes the "fidgety" adult.

> As youngsters move into adolescence, overt hyperactivity frequently diminishes.

Concluding Remarks

Although hyperactivity may be very noticeable in some ADD youngsters, it should not be considered the sole criterion for making a diagnosis of ADD. Remember, the hallmark traits are distractibility, impulsivity, and, sometimes, hyperactivity. Fortunately, hyperactivity is one of the manifestations of ADD that is very responsive to stimulant medication. Teachers must be open-minded and understanding in trying to deal with hyperactivity, always remembering that the increased motor activity is an automatic response pattern that the child cannot fully control.

Student Monitor Passes

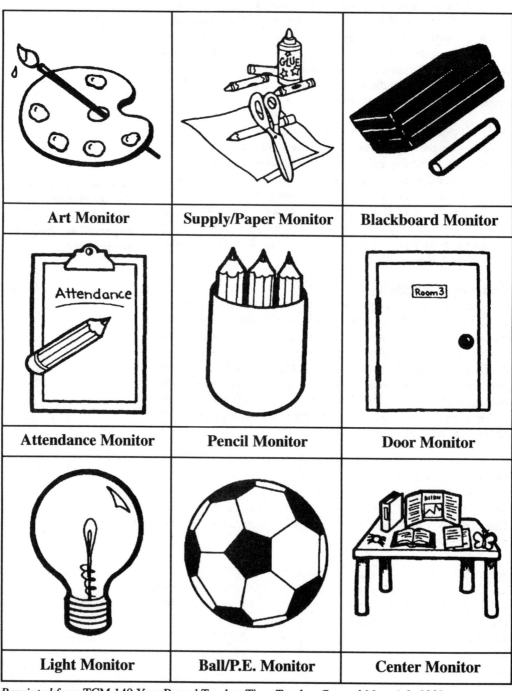

Art Monitor	**Supply/Paper Monitor**	**Blackboard Monitor**
Attendance Monitor	**Pencil Monitor**	**Door Monitor**
Light Monitor	**Ball/P.E. Monitor**	**Center Monitor**

Reprinted from TCM 149 Year-Round Teacher Tips, *Teacher Created Materials,1991*

Procrastination

Why People Procrastinate

Procrastination is a terrible problem for ADDers. Although everyone procrastinates from time to time, the ADDer does it as a way of life. Procrastination refers to postponing or avoiding tasks, obligations, work, or assignments. The longer one procrastinates, the more difficult it is to control. It is as though there is an almost palpable barrier which keeps the procrastinator from getting started. Finally, having waited until the very last minute, there is no more turning away. Many ADDers report that they work best under the pressure which comes from having delayed their work until the last minute. However, many more ADDers report terrible stress and poor performance resulting from procrastination.

> Although everyone procrastinates from time to time, the ADDer does it as a way of life.

Amazingly, there may be a scientific explanation for reports of working better under pressure, since fear may produce changes in brain chemistry. These changes resemble those which occur when a stimulant drug is taken. These biochemical changes allow the ADDer to push through his inertia, to hyperfocus, and to get the task accomplished.

In order to wage a more effective battle against the plague of procrastination, one must understand what makes it happen, especially in the ADDer. Everyone realizes that if there is something enjoyable to do, procrastination never enters the picture. Therefore, at the simplest level, procrastination has to include an element of not enjoying or not really wanting to do something. The avoided activity must contain negative elements for the person involved. People usually do not avoid pleasure, but they certainly do not rush into pain.

ADDers also tend to have playful, childlike components in their personalities. They always want to have fun. Sitting down and writing a paper or completing homework does not come under the heading of fun. The trick to overcoming procrastination is to engage discipline, control impulsivity, and see the long-range benefits of dedicated work so that, ultimately, the end results tend to be satisfaction, pleasure, and elevated self-esteem. In other words, success is fun.

Fear of Failure

For the ADDer, fear of failure is the other major factor in procrastination. Or, as twelve-year-old R.J. put it, "Procrastination is fear." Self-doubt and low self-esteem, based on previous frustrations and failures, factor into the mix. The idea is that failure may beget more failure. No one wants to fail yet again. The opposite is also true— success leads to more success. The more successes an ADDer achieves in school and in other areas, the less likely he is to postpone necessary tasks. There is more positive expectation that the work will have gratifying results, not painful ones.

Another cause of procrastination is that ADDers tend to be perfectionists who would rather not do something at all than do it less than perfectly. Frequently, when they do start a project they tend to bog down trying to perfect every detail and end up abandoning the entire project.

Effects of Medication

Fortunately, stimulant medication can mobilize discipline and motivation. As Eric, 26, says, "Before Dexedrine, all I wanted to do was work as little as possible, put off school assignments, and have as much fun as possible. On Dexedrine, everything was reversed. It became work now, get it done, and feel good that it's getting finished. If there is any time left for play, then I'll play." Andrew, 16, a high school student, describes his medication as, "...forcing me to grow up, to stop avoiding responsibility, and get on with work that needs completing."

For the ADDer, fear of failure is the other major factor in procrastination.

Many youngsters notice that their ability to function is vastly improved on medication and that they are much more likely to be successful at their efforts than before. They are more likely to buckle down to their homework or assignments earlier. Any ADDer who triumphs over his tendency to procrastinate will be well served for the rest of his life, not only as a student but also in whatever occupation he chooses.

Strategies

The best overall strategy for teachers and parents to embrace in helping ADD youngsters overcome procrastination is to do everything possible to facilitate academic successes. Parents and teachers need to make a special effort to teach strategies for discipline and self-monitoring, since these traits do not come naturally to ADDers. The sink or swim, hands-off approach to a child's procrastination has a tendency to backfire. Students with ADD often get so far behind and discouraged that they become immobilized. The resulting failure only reinforces the youngster's sense of hopelessness and starts a vicious cycle of procrastination, failure, and more procrastination.

Students with ADD often get so far behind and discouraged that they become immobilized.

The following strategies can help teachers and parents to deal with students' tendencies to procrastinate:

Strategies for Teachers

- ◆ Use assignment calendars. Sign off if necessary.
- ◆ Communicate. Talk to parents as soon as you notice missing work. Talk to the student early so failure is not inevitable.
- ◆ On long-term projects, set a series of dates for progress checks.
- ◆ Use a homework hotline, if it is available, so parents can monitor a child's homework.
- ◆ Put major assignments in writing; get parent signatures to know that parents are aware of assignments.

Strategies for Parents

- ◆ Check assignment calendars daily. Have teachers sign off if necessary.
- ◆ Sit down with your child to make a time schedule (for the day, for the week). Schedule breaks in homework so tasks do not seem insurmountable.

- Teach your child to do less enjoyable tasks first so these tasks do not continue to loom ahead.

- Break large tasks into steps, building in breaks and/or rewards.

- Use positive reinforcement to reward accomplishment. Visual reinforcement (e.g., a calendar with stars for completed tasks) can be helpful.

- Role model. Parents can do necessary work alongside the student, role modeling the importance of doing homework.

- Use tutors. Parents can break free of the frustrating homework battle by bringing in an outsider. This can be expensive, but many high school students make great tutors for elementary and junior high students, and they do not charge much. Youngsters know when the tutoring is scheduled and are less likely to misbehave with outsiders than with parents.

Success in overcoming procrastination tends to beget more success.

Concluding Remarks

A tendency to procrastinate is a core trait of ADD. The best antidote is having an awareness of the problem and developing specific, individually tailored coping strategies. Success in overcoming procrastination tends to beget more success. Fortunately, procrastination is one of the traits that responds most positively to the effects of stimulant medication.

Teacher to Teacher

The Positives and Negatives of ADD Students

ADD students in a teacher's classroom can be both a blessing and a curse. The bad news is that they can disrupt your best laid plans. One ADD student can seem to take more of your time and effort than ten others. They lose things all the time; they forget to take books home or bring homework back; and the insides of their desks, back-packs, and notebooks are a mess!

But there is good news, too. These students can be the most origi-nal, creative, fascinating people you ever have taught. You will be caught up in their intense enthusiasms—and so will your class. These youngsters find new approaches to their assignments (when they remember to do them!). And they come up with the darnedest ideas. They can be funny, inventive, talented, daring, sensitive, and compassionate.

All of this leaves the teacher with a challenge. How can one nurture the spirit, channel the energy, and help the student to achieve? How can a teacher find a way to achieve success when the child's nature dooms the child to failure in most traditional classrooms?

> ADD students in a teacher's classroom can be both a blessing and a curse.

"Equality" vs. "Fairness"

Believe it or not, there actually are many teachers out there who, despite years of experience to the contrary, deny that ADD even exists. They have done things in a certain way for years, and they are not about to change! They see little "Tommy" as a spoiled, undisciplined child whose parents obviously have not trained him properly and now want the school (or the teacher) to make up for their failure. Well, these teachers will have none of that! What "Tommy" needs is "discipline," and if he cannot follow the rules, then too bad! In spite of the fact that students with ADD are covered by the Federal Rehabilitation Act of 1973, section 504, which legally mandates that schools and teachers must make necessary accommodations for these students, old ways and attitudes are hard to change.

> To be fair is to give each student what he or she needs in order to learn.

One of the main reasons that some teachers give for opposing modifications for students with ADD is that they feel they are not being fair to other students in doing so. However, fair does not necessarily mean equal. Just as some students need eyeglasses to be able to see, or more or less food to remain healthy, or more or less sleep to feel rested, some students learn best in one way and some in other ways. Some students can focus just fine without medication, and some students cannot. To be fair is to give each student what he or she needs in order to learn.

Do Individual Accommodations Take Extra Time?

Another common assumption is that making accommodations for individual students, such as signing off assignment sheets or writing notes to parents, will take too much time. However, most teachers who are practiced at making such modifications say that they actually save time—time spent in student, parent, and administrative conferences about the student who is failing; time spent designing and supervising remediation; time dealing with classroom disruptions; time spent in chasing down missing and lost materials and assignments—in other words, the principle that applies here is that a stitch in time saves nine. The teacher who makes modifications which foster a student's success is not just helping the student's self esteem. A teacher's ego, too, is affected when a student does poorly. Preventing failure is good for everyone!

As a teacher, you already have taken a step to help these students by using this book. Your desire to learn about ADD and to help the student who has it is a clear indication that you are not one of those immoveable teachers. You are open to new information. You are willing to take risks and try new strategies. You remember why you got into teaching—to make a difference for students!

How to Deal with ADD Students in Your Classroom

The later portion of this chapter will give you a specific list of classroom modifications which will be useful in dealing with ADD students. But the most interesting thing about these often-recommended strategies is that they really are beneficial to almost all of your students. Most students learn better when they are active, rather than passive, learners. Very few educators today advocate education by lecture and worksheet—for anyone! Most students need instruction in study skills; skills, after all, are not born but learned. What student would not benefit from being given choices and chances to bring in his or her own interests to the learning process? Teachers who design their classrooms and their lessons to accommodate students who learn in divergent ways will soon discover that they are becoming better teachers!

As you become more aware of ADD in your classroom and more willing and able to accommodate students with ADD, it is very important for you as a teacher to understand just what your job is and just as important to understand what it is not. More than anything else, the teacher is an observer, a facilitator, and a communicator. The teacher's expertise and responsibility lie in the area of designing an academic program that is geared to the particular child's needs. In addition, the teacher is in the best position to observe the child in the situation that is the most inherently stressful one in the lives of most ADDers, school. The teacher, therefore, becomes the person who must communicate these observations to others who are interested in this child's progress, mainly to parents, counselors, and treatment professionals. Often, it is the teacher who has the responsibility for implementing aspects of a treatment plan (such as administering medication or making necessary classroom modifications) and giving requested feedback about whether the plan is working or not.

> If the teacher has a student who exhibits the characteristics of ADD, the teacher's most important job is communication.

The teacher must remember, however, that in no way is he or she a diagnostician. If the teacher has a student who exhibits the characteristics of ADD, the teacher's most important job is communication.

Communication should be made to parents as soon as the teacher notices a problem, such as impulsive behavior, missing homework, inability to sit still or attend, a noticeable difference between the teacher's perception of a student's ability and the student's performance on tests, difficulties in social relationships, or anything else that, to the teacher, seems not quite right. The teacher also may wish to communicate with a student's counselor, take a look at records and scores from previous years (something which, by the way, is better left undone unless there is a problem—sometimes previous teachers can transmit prejudices which are best left unseen until a teacher has formed his or her own impression of a student), check with the school nurse, or chat with the student's other teachers. The following are several scenarios about how such communication with parents might take place.

How to Communicate When There Is a Problem

The way in which communication about ADD or learning problems takes place is all-important. Most of the time, the teacher will be in a situation where the student exhibits the characteristics of ADD, but the teacher has not been informed that there is any diagnosis of ADD. A telephone call home is in order, and a great deal will depend on this first contact. If the teacher comes off as angry, exasperated, or punitive ("Mrs. Smith, I just do not know what to do with Billy. He's naughty, noisy, undisciplined, disorganized, and downright lazy!"), the parent most likely will become angry and defensive, and the outcome will not be positive. The teacher and the parent will become adversaries, and neither will be able to help the student.

> The way in which communication about ADD or learning problems takes place is all-important.

If, on the other hand, the teacher expresses concern and compassion and simply reports what has been happening and what she has observed about the child, the parent often is gratified by the contact. After all, usually the parent is concerned and worried about the very same issues at home. Sometimes, the teacher will discover that the parent knows or suspects that the child has ADD. In fact, sometimes the teacher will discover that the child already is under the care of a professional and may already be on medication. At this point, the teacher can begin working with the child, the parents, and/or other school personnel to develop the best strategies for this particular child.

Respect Dignity and Privacy

The teacher may wonder why he or she has not been informed if the parents already know that the child has ADD. The answer to this question usually lies in the parents' and child's previous negative experiences within the school system. Being special or different in any way often carries such a negative stigma for children, especially if they have been singled out or handled without respect for their privacy or their dignity. The teacher who says, in front of the entire class, "Johnny, you're getting hyper again. Did you take your medicine this morning?" or the school system that allows the nurse to come onto the loudspeaker (true story!) and broadcast throughout the school that a child needs to report for medication are ensuring that the parents of such children will do their very best not to involve the school in their child's care any time soon! A contact from a teacher who understands and cares about the child's needs, including the needs for dignity and privacy, usually is greeted with joy and relief.

Be Prepared to Give Factual Information

Another common scenario for a teacher communication with parents is the discovery that a parent has perceived a problem but does not know where to turn or how to begin to handle it. The parent may have little information or awareness about ADD or specific learning disabilities or may have a great deal of misinformation, based on popular myths. Two great areas of misinformation tend to be the "evils of drugs" and the "I thought they outgrow it" theory. Again, in this situation, the teacher is not a diagnostician. He or she might ask gently, "Have you considered the possibility that Spencer might have Attention Deficit Disorder or some learning problem? I have seen several students who have had similar difficulties, and they have been diagnosed with these conditions." In our experience, most parents are very open to such information and most will actively seek help, including books to read and referrals to diagnostic professionals. In such instances, teachers should be aware of their own districts' policies on making such referrals and follow these policies. The well-educated teacher can provide factual information on what ADD and learning disabilities are, as well as providing hope and encouragement to parents who need to deal with the fact that their child has a problem.

> Two great areas of misinformation tend to be the "evils of drugs" and the "I thought they outgrow it" theory.

What the teacher must not do is confirm a diagnosis ("Yup, Spencer has ADD if anyone does!") or deny ("Spencer? ADD? Not in a million years!") nor should the teacher either encourage or discourage medication. What the teacher should do is offer to cooperate in a treatment program, observe and report on the child's progress, and modify what happens in the classroom so that the child receives the most benefit.

The Teacher as Advocate

In some cases, the teacher is forced to become an advocate for his or her student. This is not an easy role to play. In a worst case scenario, such advocacy can be frustrating and even heartbreaking. Nonetheless, a caring teacher feels obligated to try on behalf of his or her student. In the most unfortunate situations, the teacher discovers through parent contact that there are parents who just do not care. Only the strongest and brightest of youngsters will survive such homes.

Involve the Child in Modifications

So, how do you go about modifying your classroom for the ADD student? There is no magic formula that will work for everyone. We need to remember that ADD students, like all people, are unique individuals. The same strategies do not always have the same effects on unique individuals. Each person requires his or her own plan.

The Classroom Modification Checklist on pages 45 through 51 is very useful as the centerpiece of a conference which includes the student and parent(s) and may include the child's counselor and/or other teachers. Using the checklist, a modification plan can be developed which takes into account what works best for the individual child, as well as what is possible for the individual teacher working within a given system. Obviously, including the child in designing a program is the most likely way to get the student's cooperation and willingness to participate. Asking a student, "What is your plan for getting your homework done?" or "How can you record your homework assignments so that you'll remember them?" tells professionals about this child's style and gives them a starting point to work with the child, not in opposition. As a teacher you should remember that if you do not know what will work, talk to the student. He or she might know the answer.

Obviously, including the child in designing a program is the most likely way to get the student's cooperation and willingness to participate.

Some of the strategies that follow might almost seem to contradict one another (e.g., seat the student with a role model vs. seat the student by himself). These seeming contradictions reflect the individuality of the ADD student. The best way to see the suggested modifications and the checklist is as a menu of selections. The experienced teacher must select what works best.

The Best Teacher for an ADD Student
The best teacher for an ADD student is one who is able to create a predictable structure (e.g., the homework is always on the chalkboard; the last five minutes of every class are devoted to explaining the next assignment). These students need structure. They need predictability and are upset by changes and disruptions of their routines. They need repetition so that patterns become ingrained.

Yet, this same teacher needs to be able to be flexible, to change style when interest is flagging or understanding is difficult. The best teacher for ADDers is one who is creative and amusing. The ADD student seeks excitement. If he or she does not find it in the lesson that is going on, attention will flag and the student's mind will wander to something else. Imaginative, exciting, creative teaching can hold this student's attention. For example, this ideal teacher rarely lectures; when he does, the lecture can be turned into a game with a quiz at the end to see who has the facts. Or, lecture can be used to teach study skills, such as a lesson on note-taking where at the end of class students might be asked to check their notes and highlight the ten important bits of information that the teacher wants them to have. The teacher has not just lectured but guided the students in picking out what is important and helped to highlight their notes so that future studying is easier.

Give Students Choices

The ideal teacher for ADD students creates interest by allowing students to have choices wherever possible. If what one is trying to teach is reading or writing, it seems obvious that a student will be far more motivated to do these activities if he or she is reading or writing about something interesting and real. Math becomes far more interesting if it can be used to solve real problems. One student made it through the drudgery of learning to letter in a drafting course by writing sarcastic/funny letters of protest to the teacher who replied in kind. Another student who balked at copying and memorizing spelling words each week had no trouble turning out impeccably rhymed poems using the same words. A student who could demonstrate that he had mastered a concept was not required to do thirty repetitive math problems for homework. Instead, he was asked to write a paragraph on how the concept could be used or to draw the concept as a picture. Keeping up with students' interests, such as their music, popular television shows, toys, games, or films, helps the teacher to use illustrations and examples and to create projects that will involve students.

The fear of being wrong can be paralyzing for students, especially ADD students.

The ideal teacher is not a know-it-all. He or she models being a learner. The teacher learns with the class and shows that it is O.K. not to know all the answers. One teacher has said, "Just think about it. Every time you get in front of people, common words that you wouldn't even worry about spelling, all of a sudden you say, 'Is this right? Are there two t's or one?'" This teacher's students feel free to tell her that she has made a mistake—and when they do, she says thank you! The students learn that being wrong is all right, as long as one is willing to learn from mistakes.

The fear of being wrong can be paralyzing for students, especially ADD students. The teacher who focuses less on the right or wrong answer and more on problem solving, gathering information, and exploring ideas can be the ideal teacher for an ADD student. This teacher encourages questions and discussion. The teacher calls on all of the students and finds ways to ensure that all students have their say. Nobody's attention can wander because this teacher calls on people whether or not they have their hands up. If a student has nothing to say, the teacher is not punitive. Instead, the teacher prepares that student to be called on again: "Tommy, I want you to think about that question for a few minutes, because I'll be coming back to you." And she does come back, so students (including ADD students) are much more likely to be focused because they are aware that someone notices when they are focused and when they are tuned out.

41

The ideal teacher for ADD students is also a role model in treating each student with dignity and respect. The teacher's everyday behavior should reinforce the value of each person and his or her ideas. This ideal teacher also models the value of listening and the value of structure, study skills, and organizational strategies. The teacher shares his or her own techniques for staying organized. The teacher's modeling demonstrates that people can learn coping strategies; nobody is born with them.

The Teacher Models Learning Strategies

One teacher, for example, uses sticky notes to stay organized. When writing with her students, this teacher often writes ideas on various slips of paper and moves them around before finalizing a composition. Sticky notes are always available in class for note-taking during book discussions. The students soon observe that the teacher's books are always plastered with them. They laugh at finding sticky notes on the classroom door, reminding the teacher of things to take home, or on the table, reminding the teacher of things to say to students. Soon, many students start carrying their own packs of sticky notes. The teacher has modeled a successful organizational strategy of her own, and the students have absorbed and adopted it.

More Techniques for Getting Organized

Lynda is a teacher who has ADD herself. She teaches her students organization by modeling on a daily basis several techniques that she uses to help herself to organize. All students are required to have assignment calendars. If students cannot afford these, Lynda has weekly assignment calendar sheets printed for them. Lynda makes sure that students use these calendars every day by incorporating a time in the class period to have students write down their assignments. When there is no homework, students write this down in their assignment calendars. This teacher has also found the color coding of assignments to be useful. Just by color, students can tell whether a sheet contains spelling words or math problems or a long-term project. Lynda also knows the value of putting important assignments in print for students rather than just having students copy them. Another modification that Lynda has made for ADD students is to have a second set of books for them to keep at home, since they often are forgetful. She says she knows this after years of frustration because of forgetting books herself.

Teach Students How to Be Students

So, the ideal teacher for ADD students spends a great deal of time teaching how to be a student, not just transmitting subject matter. Many teachers say, "Nobody teaches you how to be a teacher." The same might be said of being a student, that all too often, nobody

The teacher's everyday behavior should reinforce the value of each person and his or her ideas.

teaches you how. We teachers need to teach how to plan, how to organize, and how to learn, not just what to learn.

Recognize Various Learning Styles

The ideal teacher for ADD students recognizes that students have various learning styles and that there are many sensory pathways into the brain. The teacher recognizes that some students learn best visually, some by hearing, some by doing. Some do best with more than one input, so skilled teachers give students information in at least two forms, such as written on the board and oral or written on a handout, on the board, and oral. Some students function best on their own; others work best with others. The teacher tries to provide equal opportunities for all learning styles.

When "the Rules" Do Not Work

The best teachers for ADD children not only have clear rules and expectations but also use their heads and their hearts to tell them when and how to modify the rules. These teachers know when a stretch break can bring a class back on track, when to send an ADD student on an errand because he just cannot sit still at a particular moment, when a little silliness can break tension, and when less is more with homework assignments. The teacher cares enough to choose to do what is right for the students. The teacher cares enough to take the initiative to help the child and not wait until the child fails. The teacher communicates praise, not just criticism, and rewards effort, innovation, and improvement, not just conformity and high test scores.

The best teachers for ADD children not only have clear rules and expectations but also use their heads and their hearts to tell them when and how to modify the rules.

Setting Up the Ideal Classroom

The ideal classroom for the ADD student would be set up to screen out intrusive outside stimuli, such as noise from traffic, passersby, or other groups, such as students on the playground. Loudspeakers would be turned off and interruptions kept to a minimum. The room would be furnished and arranged flexibly so that both group and individual activities could take place with a minimum of disruption. Students would not have to spend the whole day sitting in uncomfortable chairs. There would be carpeting to control noise and to accommodate those who concentrate best when sitting cross-legged or lying on the floor. There would be some nice soft chairs or beanbags for quiet, comfortable reading or listening. The room would provide visual stimulation through engaging, curriculum-related materials. But it would also have an area of visual calm for those who need that for concentration. There might be quiet music playing when people work. Believe it or not, sometimes ADD kids concentrate better when they work to certain kinds of music which tends to screen out irritating noises. In fact, a little pleasant music can make quiet work smoother and more pleasant for an entire class. And when the teacher wants everyone's attention, making the music louder is a good way of getting everyone to notice.

In this classroom, students would be allowed to get up and move around as they work, picking up materials, depositing papers, consulting with one another. There would be specific places for students' materials to be collected and saved. Classroom materials also would have their specific places. There would be extras of things like books, pencils, and calculators so forgetting something at home would not be such a big deal. And the teacher would encourage the use of real-world tools, like calculators and dictionaries, not forbid it. Dr. Mel Levine (1990), an expert on ADD, has raised the question of what one would do in the real world if one misplaced his calculator and had calculations to do. The answer, of course, is not, "Do it in longhand." The answer is, "Find your calculator." Schools need to encourage students to use all of the aids available to them and instruct in their use. In the ideal classroom, the teacher would remind everyone about clean-up time, and there would be time to get one's belongings in order. The teacher would even offer to help people who seem to have a rough time getting organized.

Getting Rid of Time Pressure
In the ideal classroom, students would have plenty of time for their work. Those who finished early would have a variety of activities (e.g., computer, pleasure reading, educational games, catching up on homework) to keep them busy while others finished. Tests would not be taken under time pressure and would be designed to test what the student really knows, not just how fast he can mark the right answer. Students would receive many chances to show what they know, not just a few big tests. Assessment would be ongoing and authentic. Time pressure can send an ADD student into a panic. The student may know all the information but become paralyzed by the ticking of the clock. Even the venerable College Board gives the SAT tests untimed to students who have been diagnosed with ADD. Surely, the classroom teacher can do the same! Removing time pressure is probably the most commonly requested modification for ADD students. Experience with ADD students has caused some teachers to move away from time pressuring any students on tests. The results have been improved scores and no real loss of significant classroom time.

Classroom Modifications Checklist

Use the following checklist to create a modification plan for an individual student. For the greatest likelihood of success, try to involve the student and parent(s) in setting up this plan.

I. Communication

_____ Send home a weekly progress report.

_____ Fill out an observation checklist as requested by the child's physician.

_____ Make early and frequent contact with the child's home (do not wait for progress reports and quarterly grades). Call immediately in case of missing assignments, poor performance, or behavioral problems.

_____ Inform parents of future assignments, especially long-term assignments.

_____ Involve staff professionals when there are problems.

Additional Accommodations _____

II. Arrangement of Classroom

_____ Seat the student near the teacher.

_____ Seat the student near a positive role model(s).

_____ Stand near enough to observe and cue the student while giving directions and/or presenting lessons.

_____ Seat the student away from distracting stimuli (e.g., view, window, doorway, noisy or high traffic area).

_____ Increase the distances between desks to avoid distraction by other students.

_____ Move around the classroom to be sure students are on task.

_____ Provide a quiet area for concentration.

Additional Accommodations _____

Classroom Modifications Checklist *(cont.)*I

_____ Make sure that directions and assignments are written down and thoroughly understood before the student leaves each day. It is up to the teacher to check with the student and not depend on the student to check with the teacher.

_____ Print handout of major assignments in addition to giving verbal instructions. Have parents sign off to make sure they are aware of long-term assignments.

_____ Model what you want students to do. Act as the learner. Have students practice and model for one another.

_____ Increase visual aids and visual reinforcements, such as the following: graphic organizers, key points written on board or overhead; manipulatives, models, charts, diagrams, and pictures; written outlines; key points highlighted and/or underlined; rules which are posted and visible.

_____ Provide cues to keep the student on task. Arrange a private signal(s) to cue the student.

_____ Include a variety of activities in each class period.

_____ Break long presentations into shorter segments.

_____ Break long-term assignments into shorter segments with interim due dates.

_____ Encourage cooperative learning, peer tutoring, and other student interactions.

_____ Allow students to use technology (tape recording lessons, presentations and tests; type or word process to de-emphasize handwriting; calculators, electronic dictionaries, spell checkers).

_____ Avoid long lectures.

_____ Engage in discussion and conversation.

_____ Build physical movement into lesson plans. Do not require constant quiet and constant sitting.

_____ Build in choices where possible. Try to build on students' interests.

Additional Accomodations _____

Classroom Modifications Checklist *(cont.)*

_____ Simplify complex directions. Break them into steps. Check for understanding.

_____ Hand out worksheets one at a time instead of in a packet (less chance for losing).

_____ Hole-punch what you want kept.

_____ Provide a place in class for students to keep papers.

_____ Orally cue the student to hand in assignments. Students can do the homework and forget it.

_____ Allow students to tape record homework. Allow printing rather than cursive writing, typing rather than handwriting.

_____ Provide parent access to homework (e.g., homework hotline, mailing or sending packet).

_____ Provide structure and a predictable routine (e.g., certain days for certain types of assignments, color-coded assignments).

_____ Reduce the amount of homework. Avoid needless repetition.

Additional Accommodations _____

_____

_____

_____

_____

_____

_____

_____

_____

Classroom Modifications Checklist *(cont.)*

V. Assessment

_____ Provide training in test-taking techniques. Provide practice in different types of tests and assessments before administering the real thing.

_____ Give frequent, short assessment opportunities rather than infrequent long ones.

_____ Provide varied types of assessment opportunities rather than only one or two ways of demonstrating knowledge (e.g., open book, oral exams, take-home tests, individual and group projects, verbal and nonverbal assessments, problem-solving opportunities).

_____ Give untimed tests. Remove time pressure.

_____ Test the student individually rather than in a large group.

_____ Allow the student to take a test somewhere else where there is less distraction.

_____ De-emphasize multiple choice.

_____ Use authentic assessments and performance assessments.

Additional Accommodations _____

_____

_____

_____

_____

_____

_____

_____

_____

_____

_____

Classroom Modifications Checklist *(cont.)*

VI. Organization

_____ Make organization and study skills part of the curriculum. Teach how to organize.

_____ Provide an extra set of books to be kept at home.

_____ Provide a volunteer study buddy.

_____ Provide a list of names and phone numbers of classmates.

_____ Make sure that the student has an assignment log/calendar and is using it daily. Monitor the student.

_____ Make early and frequent contact with home. Help parents to know what work is due.

_____ Minimize disruption and any change in routine. Prepare the student for change.

_____ Target specific behavioral goals for the student. Do not expect everything to change at once.

_____ Develop a reward system for improvement and progress.

_____ Provide a place for students' possessions and materials. Model organization of the student's space.

_____ Keep the classroom organized. Students need to know where things are, and be able to find them in the expected places, and be trained to replace them there.

Additional Accommodations _____

_____

_____

_____

_____

_____

_____

Classroom Modifications Checklist *(cont.)*

VII. Administrative Accommodations

_____ Place the student in smaller classes.

_____ Provide tutoring or other one-on-one assistance.

_____ Increase school/home communication.

_____ Provide a homework hotline.

_____ Schedule more demanding subjects early in the day.

_____ Provide in-service for teachers and staff on ADD.

_____ Provide times for all of the student's teachers to meet.

_____ Tailor the curriculum to the student's individual needs.

_____ Encourage teachers to use modern, interactive learning strategies.

_____ Aid the child in taking prescribed medication while preserving the child's right to privacy and dignity.

Additional Accomodations _____

_____

_____

_____

_____

_____

_____

_____

_____

_____

Classroom Modifications Checklist *(cont.)*

_____ Tell students what to do rather than what not to do.

_____ Model positive behavior. Have students model, role play, etc.

_____ Emphasize praise rather than criticism.

_____ Use a reward system (e.g., extra privileges for good behavior, improved organization, or improved work).

_____ Keep classroom rules simple, clear, and consistent. Post rules.

_____ Allow for short breaks between assignments.

_____ Allow for physical movement. Incorporate time to move during lessons.

_____ Allow very active students to run errands, hand out papers, etc.

_____ Cue the student to stay on task. Develop a personal code with the student.

_____ Protect the student's privacy/dignity. Avoid singling out the student.

_____ If possible, allow a difficult student a time out. Do not handle discipline when either of you is emotional.

_____ Ignore inappropriate, restless, or attention-getting behavior (tapping pencil, twirling hair, bouncing foot) unless the behavior is disruptive to the class.

_____ Catch the student being good. Praise the student.

_____ Create a behavior contract. Involve the student in developing short and long term goals.

_____ Increase the immediacy of rewards.

_____ Allow natural consequences to develop, if they do not endanger students.

_____ Allow for logical consequences rather than consequences which have no relationship to the problem.

Additional Accommodations _____

_____

_____

Concluding Remarks

If the ideal classroom sounds like yours, then you are already on the way to helping ADD students, not to mention all students. However, if your classroom is arranged with military precision in neat rows and if you find yourself saying any of the following: "Sit still! Pay attention! Be quiet! Face forward! Calm down!" several times a day, often to no avail, then you need to rethink what is happening in your classroom and to seek teaching strategies which will encourage the students' active involvement in their learning rather than rewarding passivity. The above strategies will be helpful to many students, not just those with ADD. A concerned teacher can make the difference between a student's sense of success or failure, not only in school but also in life.

Social Skills

Why ADD Children May Have Poor Social Skills

At their best, ADD children can be charming, witty, spontaneous, curious, stimulating, caring, compassionate, and inventive. There is never a dull moment around ADD children. Their novel approach to problem solving and their insatiable curiosity can serve as catalysts to bring a group to new levels of understanding.

On the other hand, other ADD traits can be social liabilities. The majority of ADD youngsters experience more than their share of social problems, particularly in the area of peer relationships. The youngster's distractibility may make it difficult for him to focus on what is important in the social interaction. Impulsivity can cause a child to blurt out thoughts or ideas in the middle of an unrelated conversation or to intrude herself into an ongoing conversation without waiting her turn. Impulsivity, coupled with a short attention span and a tendency to become easily bored or frustrated, may cause the youngster to quit a group activity or suggest switching to a new one when everyone else in the group is actually having a good time. The child's distractibility can cause him to miss important instructions or information in class. When this youngster is called upon or raises a question which demonstrates his lack of awareness of what has been

> The majority of ADD youngsters experience more than their share of social problems, particularly in the area of peer relationships.

53

going on, this child often becomes a target for ridicule by classmates and for frustration from the teacher.

Unfortunately, despite the ADDers' intuitive talents for understanding some deep aspects of human nature, they can suffer from a relative lack of awareness of how people relate in social situations. In social situations, ADDers can have great difficulty perceiving the meaning of subtle social cues, such as facial expression, tone of voice, posture, and body language. A tendency to be self-absorbed does not allow the ADDer to process these vital cues so that he can successfully integrate into the group. Sometimes the ADDer will fail to process even direct communication from his peers, such as "Stop it," "You're bothering us," "You're interrupting," or "Wait your turn."

Often, the ADD youngster can relate extremely well to adults, who typically find this youngster to be precocious, interesting, and stimulating. Of course, adults tend to be more patient in social interactions than the youngster's peers, who often can be brutal with children who lack social graces. It does not take much for any youngster who behaves in a different manner from his peers to become a social outcast. Many ADDers become targets for bullies and are routinely harassed at school. This abuse prohibits them from focusing on their studies and can even cause them to be reluctant to go to school.

Teachers Can Become Frustrated

In the classroom, the ADD youngster can frustrate and annoy the teacher. Even though most teachers would never willingly stigmatize a child, at times the teacher may communicate his own frustration to the class; this only serves to reinforce the students' rejection of the youngster. A teacher is at greater risk of losing control of this frustration when the teacher does not recognize that the child's inept behavior is not willful or volitional but is part of the complex of behaviors associated with ADD.

Social Skills on the Playground

Very often, the most hurtful and negative peer interactions occur when the children are not under the direct gaze of the teacher—at recess, on the playground, in the lunch room, and during other less closely monitored times. On the playground, for example, physical activity can be wonderful for the ADDer by allowing him to release pent-up energy so that he will be more focused when he goes back to class.

ADD and Sports

Many ADDers find the typical team sports, such as basketball, soccer, or football, to be confusing and overwhelming because so much is going on all over the place at one time. These same youngsters, on the other hand, may do marvelously well in individual sports, such as tennis, swimming, wrestling, gymnastics, martial arts, and golf. Unfortunately, these individual sports are less available than team sports at elementary and junior high levels. Since, in most schools, athletics confer higher prestige among a child's peers, failure to engage in such activities can only serve to lower self-esteem.

ADDers who have been able to participate successfully in individual or team sports seem to have their confidence shored up and report fewer social problems. One can assume that these youngsters may have had more social skills to begin with so that it was easier for them to get onto the teams or participate in the individual sports.

The Role of the Concerned Teacher

How can the concerned teacher help these sensitive youngsters to develop good social skills? The most important key to success in this area is for the teacher to establish a code of conduct for all students which includes tolerance, fairness, respect for differences, kindness, and, basically, treating others with the same dignity and respect that everyone wants for himself. The teacher must model this behavior in his or her treatment of students. This ethic and code of behavior must be made clear to all students from the beginning. Since most ADDers seem to have a deep seated sense of justice and fair play, they especially will appreciate this demonstration of tolerance to all.

Teachers need to be vigilant on the playground, in the lunch room, and wherever they are serving as monitors to make sure that students are not ridiculed, harassed, or subjected to cruelty. The rule should be that such behavior is not tolerated in the school, but if it should occur, the teacher needs to be there to help and protect the vulnerable child. ADD youngsters also are vulnerable because they are very sensitive and can feel hurt quite easily. They are not very good at covering up their hurt or refraining from lashing out verbally at their persecutors. These responses only inflame the situation.

The child who becomes the target of bullies is likely to be hurt physically as well unless the child has the size, strength, or physical prowess at self-defense to ward off the bullies. A teacher or parent telling a bullied youngster to "ignore them" or "do not let them get to you" is asking for too much. The skilled teacher should intervene with some positive strategies to help the ADD child.

ADDers who have been able to participate successfully in individual or team sports seem to have their confidence shored up and report fewer social problems.

55

Remember, especially in the lower grades, teaching is as much about socialization as it is about subject matter. As the teacher intervenes in conflict situations and demonstrates how to resolve conflicts in a positive way, the teacher is making perhaps the most valuable contribution of all to the students' education.

Observe the Students' Relationships

As a preface to specific strategies for dealing with conflict resolution, the concerned teacher must be a careful observer of the relationships among students, not only in the classroom but also especially under circumstances where the children are free to interact with each other. The teacher should become aware of demographics, such as who are the leaders, who are the followers, who are the friends and what draws them together, who are the outsiders having problems with peers, and so on. Awareness of the student as a whole person, including socioeconomic background, family constellation, the presence of medical problems such as ADD, and other background information, is invaluable in dealing with students in conflict.

Each student is a unique human being who may posses specific areas of special talent. Individual teachers, as well as school systems at large, need to address and encourage these youngsters to shine in whatever they do best. For example, student athletes often are given pep rallies, but where are the rallies for student artists, debaters, actors, or storytellers? Some students are marvelous at peer counseling but never receive much recognition for this special talent. The system which celebrates all areas of student accomplishment fosters its students' tolerance for diversity in the student body. This atmosphere of tolerance lessens the likelihood that a child will be ostracized for being different or having different interests. The following specific strategies have been effective for teachers who are working on enhancing social skills.

Conflict Resolution

The teacher must master the techniques of conflict resolution. There are many programs which train both teachers and students in these important techniques, but sensitive teachers have been doing this for years without any special training and should continue to do so. Basically, conflict resolution aims to get students talking to each other to settle conflicts. Students are given ground rules, such as no name calling or interrupting, and are encouraged to tell their stories. The teacher helps the students to clarify the underlying issues which have caused the conflict and to propose solutions that are comfortable and acceptable by all parties. Effective resolution occurs when the students make a commitment to each other to abandon their old behaviors and apply the agreed upon strategies.

Basically, conflict resolution aims to get students talking to each other to settle conflicts.

Sometimes allowing each student to bring in one or two allies to the meeting facilitates the whole process of conflict resolution. Currently many schools from primary through secondary level are successfully training students in peer counseling techniques so they can act as facilitators in conflict situations. Many of these newer programs have been amazingly successful, especially since they put the emphasis for solving problems where it belongs, on the students themselves.

When to Involve Parents

In situations where these initial steps fail to bring about lasting change, we strongly urge that parents be brought into the conflict resolution process. The best format is a face-to-face meeting of all involved adults and their youngsters. Of course, human nature being what it is, there will be some parents who do not rise to these occasions. However, our experience has been overwhelmingly positive when parents have been involved. We have found that most parents wish to foster positive values in their children. The parents of bullies often are horrified to learn of their children's behavior which does not seem to reflect the values that these parents thought they were instilling. The weight of parental authority can then serve to turn the tide in favor of keeping the peace and resolving the conflict.

> Another helpful technique is to assign a student buddy or mentor to the student who is having social problems.

Buddies and Mentors

Another helpful technique is to assign a student buddy or mentor to the student who is having social problems. Often, this mentor is a student who is somewhat older and wiser, perhaps one who has been through and solved his own problems. This student can serve as a mediator, role model, support figure, and, especially, as a coach to the student who is less skilled at interacting with peers. Not only is the youngster with the problem helped, but often the mentor role is very gratifying for the student who is selected for this job.

Role Playing and Rehearsal

Another effective strategy for resolving conflicts is role playing. There are many ways to use this technique. One approach is for the teacher to work privately, one on one, with the student who is experiencing social problems. Together, they can recreate the situations which have resulted in problems and role play alternative behaviors. For example, the teacher can assume the identity of the student while the student assumes the identity of the peer with whom he is having problems. First, the teacher mimics the problem-causing behavior to get the student to look at it from a new perspective. Next, the teacher models alternative behaviors which might have elicited more positive responses. The student is encouraged to role play his new reactions to the teacher's alternative behaviors, and together student and teacher decide which behavior would work best in handling a particular situation. Once a student begins to grasp that different behaviors elicit different responses, role playing can be used not only to review past situations but also to rehearse for future social encounters. Such rehearsals help to decrease anxiety and the likelihood of further social blunders. They can increase students' confidence and ease as they encounter new experiences. As with other strategies designed to help ADD youngsters, role playing can benefit the whole class.

Rewards

Rewarding positive behavior is a time-proven technique which can reinforce the other strategies already mentioned. Praise, tokens, and certificates all have been used effectively to encourage desired behaviors. We encourage teachers to look beyond the obvious in issuing such rewards and to seek out the quieter and less public acts of kindness and compassion. Unfortunately, all too often we have seen such awards go to children who are popular and socially accepted and yet privately demonstrate insensitivity and lack of compassion to some of their fellow students. An effective alternative to the usual student of the week or month award might be a system by which all members of the school community can issue certificates recognizing individual private acts of kindness and concern.

Cooperative learning techniques can be an effective vehicle for fostering positive social interactions among students.

Cooperative Learning

Cooperative learning techniques can be an effective vehicle for fostering positive social interactions among students. For the ADD student in particular, working in a small group can help the student to focus better than in a large group and to behave in a more acceptable fashion with his peers. The teacher can enhance the student's chances for success in cooperative learning groups by preceding group work with team building activities.

Concluding Remarks

In teaching social skills, the teacher has a superb opportunity to enhance his or her students' lives, perhaps far more than by the teaching of any particular bit of subject matter. This important function of the teacher can be the most satisfying aspect of any teacher's job.

Medication

How Stimulant Medication Works

Stimulant medication appears to work by increasing the availability of dopamine, a vital neurotransmitter. A neurotransmitter is a chemical substance which carries signals from one nerve cell to another. There is evidence that at times ADDers may not produce enough dopamine for optimal functioning of the frontal and pre-frontal brain regions which are thought to act as a filter or "brake" to modulate thoughts and actions.

Stimulant medications are the most effective treatment for the core symptoms of distractibility, impulsivity, and overactivity. For the first time, youngsters are able to stay seated with reduced restlessness. They are able to hear what the teacher is explaining with less distractibility and better focus. To many youngsters, reading, which was previously difficult, becomes enjoyable and interesting. They notice that they are retaining the material, as opposed to putting in hours of effort only to find that they have no idea what they have read. The ability to control impulsivity helps the youngster to feel more in control. In fact, many ADDers remark that stimulant medication seems to allow them to feel a sense of being in control for the first time in their lives.

> **Stimulant medications hit the core symptoms of distractibility, impulsivity, and overactivity.**

Why Use Medication

Most medical specialists in the treatment of ADD (Hallowell and Ratey, 1994; Silver, 1993; Wender, 1987) agree that the use of medication is the crucial intervention in successful treatment. Giving medication for ADD often arouses parents' emotions, sometimes to the point that the child is denied even a chance to try medication. Conversely, parents of children suffering from asthma or allergies do not hesitate to administer prescribed medication on a daily basis to bring their children relief and improve their quality of life. Perhaps parents feel guilty that there is something wrong with the child. But just as searching for blame when a child suffers from asthma is pointless, neither do guilt or blame have a place when discussing ADD. Blame it on heredity, since ADD and asthma are both genetically-determined conditions.

The reason that medication is used to treat allergy and asthma is that the symptoms are brought about by biochemical and neurobiological changes which lend themselves to intervention with medication. Even though ADD does not show up in currently available blood tests, it is nonetheless a biochemical and neurobiological disorder (Hallowell and Ratey, 1994). The most modern brain imaging and brain chemistry studies are giving new understanding of ADD as a neurobiological condition (Silver, 1993). So, intervening biochemically with medication makes sense.

Media-Driven Misinformation

Today's parents are deluged with media stories about our so-called drug culture and the dangers of addiction. People are reluctant to take prescribed medication, especially for any condition which does not show on an x-ray or blood test and seems to have a willful component. The biggest problem is that the media coverage relates to drug abuse and addiction ("Just say no to drugs!") and not to the proper use of professionally prescribed medication. The result of media overkill on addiction is that the boundaries become blurred and people start to assume that even taking prescribed medication might somehow be a form of drug abuse.

Another way that parents can be frightened is by seeing a television program about ADD or reading about it in the newspaper. The media tends to dredge up controversy whenever possible on the assumption that this draws listeners or readers. Instead of getting accurate and factual reports, people frequently are exposed to misinformation and superficial coverage. Without fail, somebody will be quoted as saying that taking drugs like Ritalin can be problematic or even dangerous. Sometimes a non-medical professional or layman is quoted on the potential dangers of taking medication, creating the impression

> Giving medication for ADD often arouses parents' emotions, sometimes to the point that the child is denied even a chance to try medication.

that there still exists significant controversy. The truth of the matter is that no knowledgeable medical professional who deals with ADD has any doubt whatsoever about the need for medication in management of this problem (Barkley, 1995).

Prescribed Medication vs. Drug Abuse

Contrary to what many would assume, statistics show that youngsters with ADD who are properly medicated as soon as their ADD is identified rarely abuse stimulant medication (Barkley, 1995). On the other hand, there is a higher incidence of abuse of alcohol, marijuana, speed, and cocaine in older teenagers and adults with ADD who have not received professionally supervised treatment with stimulant medication. Most experts recognize that the abuse of drugs really represents an attempt on the part of the frustrated ADDer to find relief by self-medicating. Many adults being evaluated for possible ADD reveal a history of having tried stimulant drugs for recreational reasons and finding that the drugs were very useful in helping them to focus. This focusing effect might indicate that ADD is present.

In other words, counseling and medication tend to be complimentary and are not mutually exclusive.

Unfortunately, even if the individual has ADD, if substance abuse has become a way of life, then the physician can offer very little therapeutically unless that person realizes the destructive side of this lifestyle.

Non-specialists and ADD

Even many medical doctors, including pediatricians, who often are the first physicians consulted when parents suspect ADD or other problems, are very conservative and try to reassure parents that their youngster will grow out of it or that the child is just being a normal boy. For the longest time, many psychologists seemed to steer their clients away from taking medication, even for depression, which is now recognized to be another neurobiological condition. It is not unusual for a psychologist who has a negative bias toward medication to be assumed to be an expert on this subject, despite the fact that he is not a physician, has no training in pharmacology, and is not licensed to prescribe medication. Fortunately, in the past few years, psychologists (Barkley, 1995) have become more comfortable with the idea that medication can bring rapid resolution of their clients' suffering and may even enable the clients to participate more fully and be more productive in therapy sessions.

In other words, counseling and medication tend to be complimentary and are not mutually exclusive. Although medication is of pivotal importance, young people with ADD still need all the help and coaching they can get. The medication can reduce oppositional behavior and irritability and make youngsters much more receptive to coaching and teaching than they would be without medication. Medication does not take the place of the caring parent, the concerned teacher, or the committed therapist. Rather, medication makes these concerned people more effective in the child's life.

Medication and Academic Success

Often, the most tangible result of effective stimulant medication is significant improvement in academic performance (Barkley, 1995). Some youngsters actually go from D's and F's to A's and B's. As noticeable improvement occurs in one area of the youngster's life, it can have a ripple effect and spread to other areas by building up confidence and hope. Success replaces the old scenario of repeated failures; successful medication has the effect of enhancing motivation. The old saying, "Nothing succeeds like success" especially applies here. As the youngster begins to see positive results for his efforts, he starts to have more confidence and is less reluctant to try out new things. Stimulant medication can have a powerful reinforcing effect on motivation as it improves performance, helps the individual to feel more in control, and mobilizes the inner drive to be productive.

> Medication can have profoundly positive effects on social skills and relationships.

Social Skills and Medication

Medication can have profoundly positive effects on social skills and relationships. From the child's standpoint, the first purpose of school is to survive socially, get along with others, and feel accepted. Struggles with social skills problems are almost universal in ADDers. With medication, youngsters can focus on what others say and on their nonverbal cues. This awareness helps the ADD child socially. Being less likely to blurt out, interrupt, act hyper, or tune out makes the child less likely to be ridiculed and excluded by others.

About Specific Drugs

There is no cookbook approach to medicating for ADD. Each person is a unique individual and responds individually to a specific medication. The ideal stimulant medication is one which can be given in the morning with the expectation that it lasts through 2:00 or 3:00 in the afternoon, when school is over. All efforts should be made to accomplish this goal and avoid the need to have the youngster report to the office or school nurse for a midday dose of medication. This avoids the potential stigma if the youngster has to leave the class to get his medication. The teacher may be asked by the child's parent or physician to monitor and report on the effects of medication.

Although the name Ritalin is the one most people think of when they think of stimulant medication for ADD, there are actually five stimulants approved for treatment of ADD. These are: Dexedrine, Ritalin, Adderall, Desoxyn, and Cylert.

◆ Ritalin: For some ADDers, Ritalin sharpens focus and sustains attention better than other agents. Although Ritalin is popularly prescribed by most pediatricians and other specialists who deal with ADD, for most individuals its duration of action is only three or four hours. Although there is a long-acting form of Ritalin available, its delivery is erratic and cannot be standardized very easily. One disadvantage of Ritalin is that its effects drop off very rapidly, frequently sooner than expected.

◆ Dexedrine: Dexedrine offers convenient dosing with scored tablets, which last for 3–4 hours, and Spansules, which reliably work for 6–8 hours.

◆ Cylert: It has a long duration of action (average 6–8 hours) and is the only one available as a chewable tablet. Cylert requires more frequent blood tests to monitor liver function.

◆ Adderal: These tablets are closely related to Dexedrine, but its action lasts 4–5 hours and may cause less irritability.

◆ Desoxyn: Desoxyn is available in plain and long-acting tablets. It is a relative of Dexedrine but is longer acting (4–5 hours for plain tablets and 8–10 hours for long acting). It also has fewer side effects, such as irritability and drop-off.

Common Side Effects of Stimulant Medication

The most common side effects of stimulant medication are trouble falling asleep, loss of appetite, jitteriness, or feeling tired and disoriented. Fortunately, most youngsters can be medicated without experiencing these problems. Jitteriness and/or severe appetite suppression can be related to too high a dose but usually indicate that a different stimulant might work better.

Insomnia usually can be controlled by giving the last dose no later than five or six hours before bedtime. Conversely, there are many youngsters who actually sleep better when they are on Ritalin or Dexedrine because the drugs seem to produce a calming effect that facilitates falling asleep. The goal is to use medication so that it is still effective for evening studying but does not prevent sleep.

The most common side effects of stimulant medication are trouble falling asleep, loss of appetite, jitteriness, or feeling tired and disoriented.

Too high a dose of stimulant may cause a feeling of being out of it or disoriented. This side effect might account for some reports in the press about youngsters being given Ritalin and turned into "zombies." Since the goal of medication is to produce significant improvement in alertness and performance, it is inexcusable to allow youngsters to suffer significant side effects which undo the benefits of their medication.

Stimulants may cause irritability and/or emotionality in some individuals. However, more commonly, irritability and emotionality occur as a breakthrough when the dose is wearing off. This is called a rebound effect. These youngsters need ongoing monitoring to make sure that the therapeutic effects are being sustained and that rebound irritability is not being produced by failure to give a dose earlier.

Monitoring the Effects of Medication

No one is in a better position to monitor whether or not the medication is doing what it is supposed to than the classroom teacher. It is vitally important that the teacher communicate with the parents or, with parental permission, directly with the prescribing physician about the effects of the medication. If the child starts having academic or behavior problems, it is particularly important to notice what time of day the problems arise and if they are recurrent. Since everyone can have a bad day, including ADD youngsters, what we are looking for is a trend. If the teacher observes consistent, time-related problem behavior, she might assume that there is not enough medication in effect at that particular time.

Other variables can include the subject matter being taught. For example, many youngsters with ADD have difficulty with math and become frustrated with it extremely easily. Since it is important for these youngsters to have the full therapeutic effects of medication when math is being taught, this class should be scheduled in the morning when the medication is in full effect and when the youngster is not tired.

Although it is crucial to get data from the teacher regarding the youngster's ability to function well throughout the day, the teacher should refrain from reacting to every minor shift in emotion or activity by the ADD youngster. The teacher needs to avoid attributing all behavior to too little or too much medication. At home, just about every ADD youngster has been asked many times if a dose of medication has been forgotten because the family is picking up unacceptable behavior at that time. This is demeaning and insulting to the youngster. The best way to avoid such confrontations is to standard-

No one is in a better position to monitor whether or not the medication is doing what it is supposed to than the classroom teacher.

ize the administration and monitor effects so that the smoothest response pattern is obtained.

Avoid Humiliation When Giving Medication

The worst story of insensitivity and humiliation was reported by a psychiatrist who was visiting a school in Virginia. He said he could not believe his ears when over the school loudspeaker came the announcement, "Will Johnny Smith please report to the office to get his hyper pill." This unfortunate humiliation of the child might have been avoided if the prescribing physician had made more effort to find a medication with effects which lasted throughout the school day. If the youngster must be medicated at school, it should be done in a sensitive, tactful, and private manner.

Other Useful Medications: Prozac and Related Antidepressants

Physicians treating ADD are increasingly prescribing Prozac, Zoloft, and other new antidepressants in some youngsters and adults who have an underpinning of irritability and depression. (Hallowell and Ratey, 1994a). Interestingly, a significant number of ADDers suffer from depression, as well. Although behavioral scientists believe that depressive tendencies may be genetic, depression in ADDers also could be the result of years of disappointment and frustration. Regardless of its origin, clinical depression still should be treated medically.

Prozac also helps youngsters focus because it removes some of the emotional distress and worrying that frequently accompanies their ADD.

The newer antidepressants can be a significant adjunct to stimulant medication (Barkley, 1995). Agents such as Prozac have been nothing short of dramatic in their beneficial effects on the majority of individuals taking them. Prozac is an anti-anger pill. It can be extremely useful in youngsters who are developing oppositional-defiant behavior as a reaction to their frustration with their ADD. Prozac usually is extremely well tolerated, with only minimal side effects. Prozac also helps youngsters focus because it removes some of the emotional distress and worrying that frequently accompanies their ADD. This medication also has specific effects on reducing obsessive-compulsive behavior, which is fairly common in many children, especially if ADD is present. Individuals who are successfully treated with Prozac invariably say, "Things do not bother me so much anymore." This means that they are not being bombarded by internal stimuli of self-doubt nor are they as affected by negative inputs from others.

65

Commonly Asked Medication Questions :

Q: Are stimulants harmful to the body?

A: Drugs like Dexedrine have been available for over sixty years and have been shown to be extremely safe. Although newer agents such as Cylert may on rare occasions interfere with liver function, physicians can monitor the liver through periodic blood tests, thus allowing the safe administration of Cylert. Before placing anyone on long-term medication, the physician should do an electrocardiogram and screening blood work as a baseline. After that, repeat blood tests every year will suffice. This type of management is no different than for any person with a medical problem which requires medication on an ongoing basis.

> The most acceptable analogy to taking stimulant medication for ADD is putting on glasses in order to focus if one has a visual problem.

Q: Will I have to take this medicine for the rest of my life?

A: The answer to this one is not easy and is a decision that needs to be made by the patient and doctor together. The majority of ADD adults have noticed such dramatic changes in their ability to function and be happy when placed on the right stimulant medication that they no longer consider how long they will be on medication to be an important question. The real question might be, "What is necessary to improve and sustain the highest quality in my life?" When it comes to children and young adults, the answer is, "Yes, you should certainly plan on being on stimulants throughout your scholastic career, because being a student is one of the most taxing demands that will ever be placed on the individual, and this is where medication really shines." Not taking medication throughout one's school career can have disastrous results and cause the individual to develop a failure complex. Those adults who have struggled through with extra effort, not ever having been diagnosed with ADD, often will say how much they wished that someone had diagnosed them when they were younger and given them the medication which they are now receiving as adults. They have no doubt that things would have been very different.

Q: Isn't taking medication a crutch? Why can't I just do this on my own with willpower?

A: The most acceptable analogy to taking stimulant medication for ADD is putting on glasses in order to focus if one has a visual problem. If a child needs glasses to see the chalkboard, does anyone think of these glasses as a crutch? The answer is no, because needing glasses is such a natural and commonplace occurrence. One can think of using stimulant medication to focus and fine tune those parts of the brain which are necessary to get the schoolwork done as eyeglasses for the brain.

Q: Does tolerance build up to stimulants so that more and more pills will have to be taken with less and less effect?

A: Fortunately, the majority of ADDers find that once the right dose is determined, they can remain on this dose indefinitely into the years without making any changes.

Q: Will taking stimulants cause a person to become addicted?

A: Stimulant medication for someone with ADD is analogous to vitamin replacement therapy. It connects the missing link in the brain which keeps the individual from being maximally effective. It is extremely rare to find an ADD youngster who has been taking stimulants for a number of years to go on to abuse them (Barkley, 1995). The main problem is in the untreated ADDer who takes a wrong turn into the arena of drug abuse and keeps looking for some kind of pharmacological fix to feel better. This can be viewed as the individual's attempt to self-medicate feelings and behavior which he is aware of but does not understand.

> Many creative people turn out to have ADD, and most say that the medication helps them organize and get more done.

Q: Will a youngster taking stimulants experience decreased growth?

A: Earlier studies suggested this as a possibility, but repeat work indicates that retardation of linear growth is quite unusual. If it does occur, a maximum of 1/2" in the expected height for that person might be lost. The physician should select the stimulant which has minimal appetite-suppressing side effects. Drug holidays (times when medication intentionally is discontinued) on weekends and in the summer should neutralize any remote chance of inhibiting growth. The current feeling is that there is not enough evidence to suggest that any youngster with ADD should be denied stimulants because of the possibility of suppressing growth.

Q: Will stimulant medication stifle creativity and original thinking?

A: Many creative people turn out to have ADD, and most say that the medication helps them organize and get more done. If anything, the medication has a reinforcing and enhancing effect on creativity.

Q: How long does it take for stimulant medication to take effect?

A: You can expect noticeable benefits within hours of starting stimulant medication. Most have a quick onset of action, averaging less than thirty minutes, which allows a rapid assessment of the possible benefits of stimulants.

Q: What happens if you go off the stimulant medication? Does it take a long time to start working again?

A: Just as the onset of action is rapid, if someone stops stimulant medicine the benefits can be recaptured within 24 hours or less, so no major time is lost.

> You can expect noticeable benefits within hours of starting stimulant medication.

Q: Should youngsters take medication on weekends?

A: This depends on the academic and social demands on the youngster. Since stimulant medication can facilitate positive interaction with other people, including family members, keeping the medication going on the weekend seems like a good idea. However, if behavior at home is not an issue but academic performance at school is, then in certain cases medication can be omitted on weekends or vacations.

Q: Can stimulants be used before exercise or participation in sports?

A: Young athletes should follow their individual physicians' recommendations on this subject. For team sports participation, the athlete should let the coach know about any medication he or she is taking so that local regulations can be explored.

Concluding Remarks

Increasingly, research is confirming the biological link in ADD. Modern imaging techniques have shown changes in brain activity in ADDers. The PET scan produces colored pictures which demonstrate variations in the brain's uptake of glucose, its essential nutrient, in various regions of the brain. In addition, growing knowledge of the specific neurotransmitter sites affected by stimulants and antidepressants is shedding light on the neurobiological nature of ADD. Using medication for ADD is the state of the art in successful management. Fears of medication often are grounded in misinformation. No ADD youngster should be deprived of the chance to maximize his full potential through the use of stimulant medication. The real risk lies in not using medication, resulting in irreparable damage to the self-esteem and sense of future of the ADD youngster.

Self-Esteem

What Is Self-Esteem?

The essence of good teaching goes far beyond imparting knowledge of subject matter. Good teaching also must foster the positive self-image of each child. Self-esteem is a precious gift that goes to the very core of our being. As Mark Twain has said, "A man cannot be comfortable without his own approval."

A workable definition of the term self-esteem was offered by the California Task Force to Promote Self-Esteem and Personal and Social Responsibility. They defined self-esteem as the individual's appreciation for his or her own worth and importance coupled with a concept of accountability to oneself and the desire to act responsibly toward others. Most behavioral scientists acknowledge that self-esteem is rooted in a biologic and environmental interaction. The individual's experiences, especially responses from significant others, influence the development of self-esteem.

In the case of ADD youngsters, there is nothing more important than the issue of self-esteem. As the ADDer struggles for success and mastery, self-esteem is always on the line. Inevitably, every ADDer is at risk to develop low self-esteem. As the years go by, the young-

> Self-esteem is a precious gift that goes to the very core of our being.

ster typically experiences increasing frustration with school work, underachievement, problems making or keeping friends, frequent reprimands from adults, generally negative feedback, and a vague feeling of being different. Sooner or later, many ADDers come to regard themselves as failures, even though they may possess many talents.

Counterproductive Coping Strategies

In an attempt to ward off the painful erosion of self-esteem, some ADD youngsters may resort to counterproductive coping strategies. Teachers and parents should be alert to these and recognize that youngsters employing these coping strategies are desperately trying to prevent further damage to their already low self-esteem. Although the following behaviors may be provocative and will need to be halted, they also should be recognized as cries for understanding:

- ◆ Avoiding: "If I do not try, then I can never be accused of failing."

- ◆ Quitting: "What's the use? This isn't working."

- ◆ Clowning: "Hey, I could be doing stand-up! This certainly will get their attention."

- ◆ Bullying: "Maybe I can find somebody who feels smaller than I do."

- ◆ Cheating: "I'm tired of being called stupid all the time. So what's the harm?"

- ◆ Denying: "I hardly have any homework. Besides, there's plenty of time."

- ◆ Rationalizing: "Math is really stupid. Who uses this stuff in real life? Why do I have to know this junk anyway?"

- ◆ Impulsivity: "I lost the instructions, but who cares? Let's just get this over with."

Fostering Positive Self-Esteem

The markers of a child's positive self-esteem are confidence in his abilities, self-acceptance, and a sense of basic worth and human dignity. Developing and keeping positive self-esteem can be difficult, even if one does not have ADD. Changing a child's negative self-image takes inventiveness and hard work by parents and teachers. The good news is that ADD youngsters tend to be very resilient and, with encouragement, can turn failure into success. The most important single technique to foster positive self-esteem is to provide opportunities for genuine success and mastery such as the following:

◆ Highlight the youngster's strengths and talents.

◆ Place the student in high-ability groupings in areas of talent. Remember that giftedness does not have to occur in all areas. A child may be gifted in one area and not in another.

◆ Convey a genuine sense of hope and caring and a basic optimism about human potential. Nothing gives a child as much confidence as having someone believe in him.

◆ Do not surround yourself with colleagues who are negative toward students or teaching. Do not listen to previous teachers' negative comments. Assume the positive and allow the youngster to start the year with a clean slate. There is plenty of time to check a student's records if you perceive a problem.

◆ Model self-esteem. Your respect for yourself is contagious.

◆ Treat each person with respect and dignity, just as you expect to be treated yourself. Discipline in private. Do not make an example of any child. Do not point out a child's failings in public. If the child is taking medication, respect his or her privacy.

◆ Give the youngster responsibility. Allow a younger child to be a helper. Allow the child to act as a mentor in areas of strength. Give the child definite duties and chores, both at school and at home.

◆ Praise accomplishment. Use positive reinforcement for accomplishments rather than punitive responses to failure. Give the student time to improve. Not all students respond right away.

◆ Make sure that the child knows that he is important, loved, and wanted and that his worth as a person is not contingent upon grades or specific achievements. Try to say a personal word to each student as often as possible. Notice things—a new hairstyle or shirt, an absence from school, red eyes, or a runny nose. Noticing says that you care.

◆ Provide opportunities for problem solving. Guide the child through ways of reaching a solution rather than just giving him the answers.

Make sure that the child knows that he is important, loved, and wanted and that his worth as a person is not contingent upon grades or specific achievements.

71

◆ Provide opportunities for making choices. Allow the child to make as many of his own decisions as possible. Even if you do not like the decision, unless harm will result, allow the child autonomy. For example, clothes and hairstyles can become battlegrounds for parents and school authorities, but except in areas of health, safety, or actual disruption, these should be the child's decisions.

◆ Use mistakes as opportunities for learning. Show by example that to err is human. Share your own mistakes with youngsters. Show them how to laugh at themselves. Give them the opportunity to do something over again.

Even if you do not like the decision, unless harm will result, allow the child autonomy.

◆ Help youngsters to understand accountability. Give youngsters reminders about deadlines and due dates. Set up a system of rewards and consequences for various behaviors.

◆ Act as a coach. Teach study skills. Do not assume them.

◆ Communicate with the child's home. Communicate often about positive things. Do not limit home contacts to negatives and problems.

◆ Do not be discouraged if the ADDer has a bad day. Typically, the ADDer can take two steps forward and one step back. Inconsistency is a hallmark trait of ADD.

◆ Foster success. Do not be afraid to modify for the individual youngster. Remember that fairness means giving each student what he or she needs for success.

The following page contains a reward incentive that can be used as positive reinforcement and self-esteem booster for students in your class.

Reward

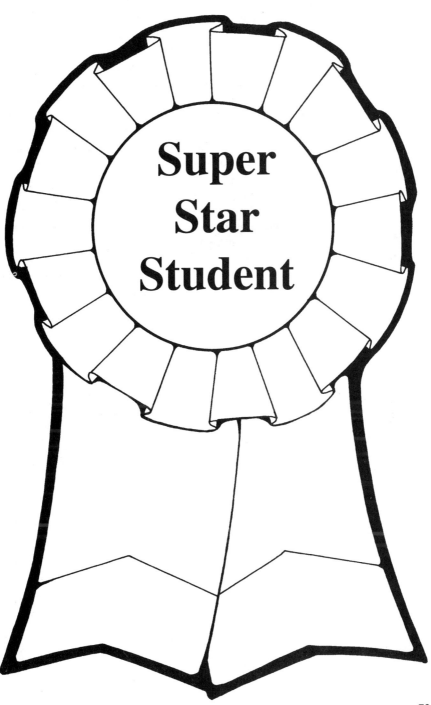

Concluding Remarks

Most successful people can look back on their earlier years and recall one or more adults who made a profound difference in their lives. Often, this person was a teacher who took a special interest in the individual. In many cases, this teacher saw creativity, talent, and potential where others did not. Having a respected adult believe in one, even if he does not believe in himself, can bring about a positive turn towards self acceptance. Acting as a mentor is one of the most satisfying and positive things that any teacher can do. Edward M. Hallowell, M.D., co-author of *Driven to Distraction* (1994), recalls with great fondness the influence of a kindly, old-fashioned elementary school teacher. Taking him under her protective wing and showing faith in him to master reading, despite his undiagnosed dyslexia and ADD, she provided the turning point in his life. Today, this prominent psychiatrist credits his elementary school teacher with his success. Her influence resulted in his becoming a physician. Remember, the fruits of your efforts may not be immediately obvious. But you can be assured that you do make a difference.

References

Barkley, R. A. (1995). Taking charge of ADHD: The complete, authoritative guide for parents. New York: Guilford.

Cousins, M. (1965). The story of Thomas Alva Edison. New York: Landmark, 1994.

Douglas, V. I. (1972). Stop, look and listen: The problem of sustained attention and impulse control in hyperactive and normal children. Canadian Journal of Behavioral Science, 4, 259–282.

Fowler, M. (1992). The CHADD educators manual. Plantation, FL: CHADD.

Gardner, H. (1983). Frames of mind: The theory of multiple intelligences. New York: Basic Books.

Grisham, D. L., & Molinelli, P. M. (1995). Cooperative learning. Westminster, CA: Teacher Created Materials.

Hallowell, E., & Ratey, J. (1994a). Answers to distraction. New York: Pantheon.

Hallowell, E., & Ratey, J. (1994b). Driven to distraction. New York: Pantheon.

Hammontree, M. (1986). Albert Einstein: Young thinker. New York: Aladdin.

Hartmann, T. (1993). Attention deficit disorder: A different perception. Novato, CA: Underwood-Miller.

Hennigh, K. (1995). Understanding dyslexia. Westminster, CA: Teacher Created Materials.

Latham, P. S., & Latham, P. H. (1992). Attention deficit disorder and the law: A guide for advocates. Washington, DC: JKL.

Levine, M. (1990). Keeping ahead in school. Cambridge, MA: Educators Publishing Service.

Shah, D. K. (1993, December 19). Steven Spielberg, seriously: Hollywood's perennial wunderkind confronts history, sentiment and the fine art of growing up. Los Angeles Times Magazine.

Silver, L. B. (1992). The misunderstood child (3rd ed.). San Francisco: TAB.

Silver, L. B. (1993). Dr. Larry Silver's advice to parents on attention deficit disorder. Washington DC: American Psychiatric Press.

Wender, P. H. (1987). The hyperactive child, adolescent, and adult: New York: Oxford.

Teacher Created Materials
Resource List

TCM 504 Portfolios and Other Assessments

TCM 651 Cooperative Learning Activities for Language Arts

TCM 656 Cooperative Learning Activities for Math

TCM 654 Cooperative Learning Activities for Social Studies

TCM 838 Authentic Assessment

TCM 842 Cooperative Learning

TCM 846 Building Communication Partnerships with Parents

TCM 848 Understanding Dyslexia

TCM 882 Teaching With Mutiple Intelligences